When we want to understand something, we cannot just stand outside and observe it. We have to enter deeply into it and be one with it in order to really understand. If we want to understand a person, we have to feel her feelings, suffer his sufferings, and enjoy her joy.

—Thich Nhat Hanh
Peace Is Every Step

Healing unfolds through engaging our experience as a whole.
—Arthur Egendorf

I will tell you something about stories. . .
They aren't just entertainment.
Don't be fooled.
They are all we have, you see,
all we have to fight off death and illness.

You don't have anything
if you don't have stories.

—Leslie Marmon Silko
Ceremony

This book is dedicated to my brave daughter.

HARD LOVE

HARD LOVE

writings on

violence & Intimacy

edited by

Elizabeth Claman

queen of swords press eugene, oregon

Editor Elizabeth Claman gratefully acknowledges a grant from the Center for the Study of Women in Society at the University of Oregon without which this anthology might not have been published.

Queen of Swords Press also wishes to thank the following people for their assistance in preparing this book for publication: Alice Evans, Leigh Anne Jasheway, Claudia Lapp, Brenda Shaw, Susan Stairs, Yvonne Vowels and Hannah Wilson. Many thanks as well to Margarita Donnelly, Rebekah Eller, Monika Fischer, Robin Hale, Linda Kintz, Dorianne Laux, Phyllis Luman Metal, Marilyn Miller-Bagley, Cheryl McLean, Clif Ross, Linda Saltmarsh, Nola Shurtleff, and John Witte for their support and encouragement.

Book design by Cheryl McLean and Elizabeth Claman.
Typesetting by ImPrint Services, Corvallis, Oregon.
Manufactured in the United States by Gilliland Printing, Inc.,
Arkansas City, Kansas.

Published in the United States by

Queen of Swords Press
PO Box 3646,
Eugene, Oregon 97403
(541) 344-0509

Library of Congress Catalogue Card Number: 96-070556

ISBN: 0-9638992-3-6 (paper)

Printed on on acid-free, unbleached, recycled paper

CONTENTS

PART IV: DARNING THE WORLD:
A JOURNEY OF TRANSFORMATIONAL HEALING

EDITOR'S FOREWORD

Editing an anthology is a strange task because no matter what the original goal for the project might be, the writing itself determines the book's final identity. In this, I am reminded of the way Michelangelo is said to have excavated the forms he sensed already alive within the marble he was carving, and of the way Zen potters practice non-attachment to their ceramics because the many forces at work in the raku process make achieving a preconceived design impossible. My original goal in compiling this anthology was to offer a forum for unheeded voices on the subject of domestic violence. But over time, as I read through the mountains of manuscripts submitted by women and men all across the country, a second idea took shape, and from that, a third. So I have many people to thank for the ultimate form of this book.

Violence within intimate relationships—which was the initial impetus for this anthology—clearly does not occur in isolation from other kinds of violence, nor can it be healed without healing other aspects of our lives. The structure of *Hard Love* reflects this premise. The four sections into which the book is divided are entitled "Twentieth-Century Landscapes/The Violence that Surrounds Us," "War Zone/The Damage We Do to One Another," "Taking Back My Name/Moving Beyond Violence," and finally, "Darning the World/A Journey of Transformational Healing." The connections between these sections have been significant to me personally because they reflect my own evolution. As a way of inviting you into the writing that follows, I would like to describe each section, and as I do, to share with you elements from my own story.

Part I, "Twentieth-Century Landscapes," depicts various aspects of the violence that permeates our culture. Wars, social turbulence, power imbalances, violence against nature and aggressions between different groups of people, all take their toll on our lives no matter how remote they may seem.

For me, the connection between global violence and intimacy was brought home as my marriage began to fall apart against the backdrop of the Gulf War in 1991. Although my husband and I were not physically or even verbally violent to one another, the images I still associate with the end of our love are burning oil refineries, "smart bombs" finding their ways down shafts, "clean strikes" killing only specific civilians, tanks scorched and overturned like so many stink bugs beside desert highways that reamed their way through desert mine fields. New and horrifying terms like "collateral damage" filled the rhetoric of politicians, and in my own home town, battle lines were drawn between those who hated and those who loved the image of the United States as the world's badass cop.

Whereas during the Vietnam war my husband and I in our separate ways had both been active in demonstrating for peace, during that brief and bitter explosion of violence in the Middle East, we were paralyzed. Unlike many of our friends who were out demonstrating, we shrank into ourselves and only watched with horror as the drama played itself out on TV. As it did, he and I moved progressively farther apart, seeing in each other a reflection of our own impotence in the face of that brutality, and in the war, a reflection of our lost faith in each other.

From my current perspective five years later, I believe that if my husband and I had opened to one another and gone to stand together in solidarity with our friends against that war, if we had talked and cried together over the devastation and then made love as a sign of our shared hope, we would have survived the war and strengthened our connection to one another. But we did not. Instead, we allowed the violence of the world to extinguish our spark of passion and compassion. The result for me was not only divorce, but a bout with clinical depression as I internalized the war and my anger at my husband and myself for giving up.

Part II, "War Zone," is dedicated to all the people—both men and women—who have been the objects of aggression in intimate relationships, or who have inflicted pain on one another. In some sense, that probably includes almost everyone.

Although I had experienced violence between various combinations of parents and step-parents when I was young, it was only when intimate violence touched my adult life that I began to think about compiling this anthology. The precise moment was just after a call from my daughter on November 23, 1993. She phoned from Germany—where she had been living for six years—crying because her lover had just thrown her out of their apartment and was hurling all her belongings into the snow. He had come home drunk from a party and began berating her, getting angrier and angrier because she wouldn't fight back. It was 1:15 in the morning there. This was the fourth time he had behaved abusively to her in just as many weeks, and she was five months pregnant with their baby.

Over the course of her pregnancy he had gradually isolated her more and more, exploding each time she made contact with anyone besides himself, but spending a lot of time away from home. He called her many times during the course of each day, checking that she was at home, sometimes dropping by unexpectedly hoping to surprise her in some wrong-doing. Often, when he would come home late at night, he would demand sex, raping her if she expressed hesitation, calling her a whore, and doing everything he could to make their intimacy painful for her. Yet, for some reason, she stayed with him.

That night in 1993, she was wearing a nightgown and slippers and the temperature was near freezing. She ran to a pay phone two blocks from her home, not knowing where to turn, and called me, 6,000 miles away, sobbing into the phone, "Mommy, I don't know what to do."

I felt so helpless at that distance. All I could do was calm her hysteria and suggest a friend she might call who would be willing to drive fifteen miles to pick her up and take her to safety—someone the boyfriend did not know.

The next day, securely settled, she called again and told me she would never go back to him. She was considering returning to the States and could she stay with me for a while?

"Of course! Come!" I told her. "I'll send you some money. Just don't go back. This has happened too many times."

Indeed, it had: rape, selling her belongings, stealing money from her, battery, verbal abuse, and in between, the passionate and tender reconciliations that seem to be an inevitable part of this dynamic. Because this pattern had been going on for months and her escapes and returns had been so public, it had become progressively harder for her to ask friends for help. They all said the same thing: "You're crazy to go back to him." And in a sense she was. After so many months of ill-treatment, she was no longer herself. He had succeeded in making her believe that his behavior was what she deserved and that she would never find a man who loved her as much as he.

Two days later when I called, the friends sheepishly told me she had returned to him, only to repeat the cycle of violence again and again until he finally hurt her so that the baby was at risk. Then, yes, she did leave, swearing it was "for good," although she bought a round-trip ticket to the States. Friends and family tried to make the separation easy for her, but the man did what so many in his situation do: he began a campaign of seduction, luring her back with promises and tears. After a month of trying to resist, she said, "It's no use, Mom, I love him and this is his baby." She returned, only to face the worst abuse yet.

Not until after her daughter was born did she finally really escape. Having the responsibility for another life changed her from a malleable and needy victim into a mother lion willing to do anything to care for and protect her child and herself. After she left, she spoke to that man only once, calling to say she would not be back. After first trying tears, he turned bitter and threatened to kill her and kidnap the baby. But rather than give in, my daughter went into hiding. For a year she lived in fear, jumping each time the phone or the doorbell rang, moving furtively from town to town, suspecting every stranger, as her ex-lover hounded her family and friends, calling us sometimes as many as fifteen times a day. Then, quite suddenly the calls stopped. We all sat still waiting for the storm to strike. But it never did.

Now, two years later, my daughter's immense capacity for love and wonder is gradually being restored. But it isn't easy. The threat of possible retribution still lurks at the corners of her world, making sleep difficult and causing her to live with extreme caution. It will be a long time before she is really free from the damage done to her, before she learns to trust another man.

Watching my own child go through the nightmare of partner abuse has given me much more understanding of the problem. I have been able to see the ways my daughter's relationship to her lover was shaped by certain myths within our culture: *Men are supposed to be strong and domineering; women subservient. Men have certain needs that women must fill no matter what their own needs are. Women like to be pushed around because it makes them feel loved. The passion of reconciliation compensates for the lover's brutality.* And so forth. Somehow, she believed that to be loved meant to be dominated, that jealousy was a sign of adoration, that only a man of intense emotions was interesting, and all the others were dull pablum.

Over the course of that traumatic year, I discovered that her inability to defend herself was also rooted in her personal history—her childhood rape by a male baby sitter, her father's emotional instability, my own selfish meanderings when she was little. Because I barely believed it myself, I failed to teach her that each of us deserves to be unconditionally and tenderly loved by the partner we choose. Recognizing my own culpability made it feel important to do something concrete to help not only my own daughter but other people as well. The result is this book, *Hard Love.*

Part III, "Taking Back My Name," records a phase of the movement toward healing. In it, writers share inspiring images of personal recovery from a wide range of traumatic circumstances. For me, the notion of taking back one's name entails much more than simply identifying with a set of sounds or letters. It implies the rediscovery of one's core sense of being. As I have learned first-hand, it is a powerful process.

While my daughter was going through her push-me-pull-you escape from her abusive lover and I was rising slowly from my post-divorce slough of despond, ironically, I myself became involved in an abusive relationship. While my lover never hit me, stole from me or raped me, he did delight in belittling me, screaming at me with no provocation, and scapegoating me for both old angers and daily frustrations. Despite this behavior, I lived with him for over a year. Then, inspired by my daughter's courage, I declared my autonomy and moved out.

I will never forget the sweetness I felt on finding myself alone again as my body released its contorted knots of nerve and muscle and my psychological outlook brightened. It was as though colors and music reanimated my perception of the world, amplifying and transforming it into something radiant and fine again.

One of the things that helped me to break free was recognizing the trap of blaming my partner for my situation. With the help of a fine therapist, I began to assume responsibility for my own acts and emotions. Once I did so, I was able to make the necessary changes. However, I must also acknowledge that my situation was not the universal norm. As some of the writings in this volume attest, there are situations which are beyond our control, and people who are truly and horribly abused. Yet whenever and however we succeed in breaking free, fighting back, reclaiming our identity and rediscovering our inner fire, it is a remarkable feeling. I am proud to share that sense of triumph and empowerment with the writers included in this section of *Hard Love.*

Healing our personal relationships is only one part of the larger movement toward transformation. Part IV, "Darning the World," gives voice to the next step in the process. Here, writers share their sense of delight in daily life and describe the particular ways they have developed healthy intimacy. Relating the work in this anthology again to my own experience, I think of the activities that have helped me heal from my failed marriage, from my abusive relationship, and from the pain of watching my child suffer.

One of my favorite sources of renewal is to walk up the mile-and-a-half trail that climbs about a thousand feet to the top of our local Mount Pisgah. Along the way, depending on the season, I am treated to an ever-changing display: the early green shoots and buds in March and April, a profusion of wild flowers from May through August, the autumn yellows, ochres and oranges of the maple and oak, the shifting hues of upland meadows from gray to green to gold to brown to gray. Whether I walk up through rain, snow, fog, or sunshine, the way is always studded with surprising and subtle beauty. On top I often sit for an hour or so, just breathing and watching the cloud patterns in the sky, the kestrels or tree swallows chasing one another in gigantic loops, and the expanse of mountains in the distance. When I am up there, the world grows big again and my sorrows and resentments shrink into perspective.

Sometimes while I walk up the trail I repeat to myself a Buddhist prayer that has become more and more meaningful to me. As I say each line, I breathe in and out, mindful of the way the air sustains me as it moves through my lungs and body.

May I be filled with loving kindness
May I be well
May I be peaceful and at ease
May I be happy

After such an outing, when I come back down to my work, my relationships, my studies, my responsibilities, everything seems deeper and gentler. I can more readily see the beauty in those around me, my ability to work is heightened, and I feel more at peace with the world, less susceptible to anger and distress.

Likewise, when I spend time with my grand-daughter I also feel renewed. Her laughter and inventiveness, her sweet unhampered affection for me, her openness and curiosity all call forth kindred responses in me. Being a grandparent is a very special gift because it allows me the opportunity to love and be loved in a unique way—free of compulsion and obligation, a pure and altruistic welling up of tenderness. It is a soft and easy love that can unravel the tight-drawn skein of old hurts and betrayals. It offers me a chance to begin over, using everything I've learned in the past thirty years since my own first stumbling initiation into parenthood. Sometimes my love toward that little being wells up so strongly that it makes me dizzy. And when it does, there are parts of my spirit that open as never before, and stay that way. This is true intimacy and it is deeply healing.

Clearly, before we can begin healing ourselves and our culture, we need to listen deeply to candid expressions of pain and acknowledge their impacts on our lives. But once we have done so, it is also important to move out into the healing light, to allow those close to us to love us and in turn, to love them and share their sorrows and their joy.

In that regard, I want to say that compiling this anthology has been a deeply healing experience for me. By reading and rereading the voices contained in these pages, I have gained a deeper understanding of human relationships at their worst and at their best, and a vital hope in the transformative power of love. I hope that reading this collection will give each of you permission to tell your story—whatever it may be—and to find healing through the many paths suggested by the authors in this book. As Deena Metzger has written in *Writing For Your Life*:

> The inner world is for each one of us—novelist, diarist, or diplomat—in our equally ordinary and extraordinary lives the essential territory where everything that might be known resides until it can be called forth into the public arena. To be willing to live within the imagination is to commit oneself to the gathering together of the pieces that might begin to form a self. To avoid this territory is to avoid the encounters that might validate, inform, or enhance one's experience.

Each of the writers in this anthology has entered that deep and mysterious inner place, then given voice to what she or he discovered there. I invite you now to join them.

Elizabeth Claman
Eugene, Oregon
August 1996

PART ONE
TWENTIETH-CENTURY LANDSCAPES
THE VIOLENCE THAT SURROUNDS US

Physical pain has no voice, but when it at last finds a voice, it begins to tell a story.

—Elaine Scarry
The Body in Pain

It is important to stay in touch with the suffering of the world. We need to nourish that awareness through many means—sounds, images, direct contact, visits, and so on—in order to keep compassion alive in us.

—Thich Nhat Hanh
For a Future to Be Possible

Remember the ones who get burned.
Their desires cut off from their hearts.
Burned by the Prince of Fire,
who sleeps waiting at the edge of vision.

—Corey Fischer, Albert Greenberg,
Naomi Newman of the Traveling Jewish
Theater, *Coming from a Great Distance*

editor's note

Reading the work in this first section of Hard Love, *I realize that my own experience—described in the foreword to this anthology—is not unique. Violence troubles all our lives even when it does not seem to impact us directly. Wars fought in distant lands, the growing exploitation of poor countries by rich ones, the decimation of our ecosystem, the dislocation of whole tribes of people—each of these events causes us to feel despair, alienation and anger.*

In several of the pieces in this section, the interaction between global, local and personal violence is made especially clear, as in Elizabeth Oakley's poem, "Blood Root," and in Ellyn Bache's story, "The Value of Kindness." In other works the connections are more subtle as in John R. Campbell's essay, "Vulnerability and Love," and Sharon Doubiago's poem, "Outlaw." While Campbell examines human impact on the environment, Doubiago allegorizes the violent underbelly of the American socio-political landscape.

Other authors address problems that arise from a more intimate confrontation with social transgressions. Emily Robertson's tough poem, "Glass Pipe Prison," takes on the violence that surrounds drug abuse, and Lisa Martinović and Robin Jacobson respond with articulate rage to the violence men direct toward women. Still other writers examine some of the broader cultural implications of violence. In two very different ways, for example, Dorianne Laux's journal entry and Amy Klauke-Minato's essay both bring home the responsibility we bear toward our children. In her poem, "Sight Lines," Elisavietta Ritchie recreates the sense of ambient fear women often feel in the face of possible danger.

These writings, like the others you will read in this section, address the many different kinds of hostility that plague our world. I have invited these poets and writers to share with you their observations—some drawn from personal experience, others rendered as fiction—in the hope that mindfulness of these broader kinds of violence will contribute to our understanding of the violence that erupts in our most intimate relationships. —**E. C.**

Katie Kingston

SET IN CONCRETE

A man is pouring cement.
A woman is clenching her fist.
A daughter throws a ball
with all her might. It catches
her sister in the eye. A full
moon coughs behind the night
tree. The sound of a tailgate
dropping. Metal and metal.
Someone's hand inside a paper bag
pulling out nails. The morning
spreads tree shade through the fields.
A voice yells, "Hi, I'm home,"
and a door clicks behind it.
A woman is clenching her fist.
The sound of the drill
against wood. Noise enters
like water through a crack. A woman
is clenching her teeth. A tiny
noise escapes. A noise that began
in her throat. The fist that hit
the daughter is stuck in the eternity
of yesterday. The violence lurking
around the corner is now marching
up Main Street as if it too
has the right for freedom of speech.
Tell that woman to unclench
her fists. Tell that man to come
home from work. Tell the children
to laugh and to get A's
on their report cards. Push the noise
back through the crack. Seal it.
Someone is throwing up in a quiet
corner. Someone is crossing
a bridge, a bag full of fists
slung over her shoulder. Someone
is planting them in the just-right
soil of afternoon.

Valerie Nieman

THINGS ARE CLOSE TO THE SURFACE HERE

In this small town we number
murders on the fingers of one hand:

A man killed his wife
for serving
green beans one more night.

A man killed his lover's husband,
shooting through a closed
door, buckshot unfurling
a Decoration Day peony
from the tight bud of his chest.

A man laid flame in the halls
of an apartment building;
a woman leaped,
shoulders winged with sinewless flame,
her hope-chest china
found white,
unbroken, after three floors collapsed.

One shot a woman pregnant with his child
in the parking lot of the police station,
under the window where a dispatcher
scowled over a needlepoint posy
and logged 10-7 calls for lunch.

No one writes this
in police reports,
but when it gets too warm in early April
quiet men start fights
because they are idle,

and old factory ways tangle their feet
like bindweeds of abandoned fields.

Black granite cannot keep
the changing names
of those lost in economic wars.
They make a slow memorial
on the courthouse square;
they wear their empty hands,
medals of obsolete conflict,
fine metal forced
into a particular shape
by a die that no longer exists.

They have all lost
something physical
though the loss may not be seen.
That man, missing
the four fingers of one hand,
another without a foot,
and him, the man whose hip joint
was fused in some impact
so that he goes swinging his leg outward,
compassing mute circles.

When the ground gives under foot
it may only be the tunneling of a mole
(that striving panicked little body)

or the land may be subsiding
into the place where coal was

or the runoff that flashes silver
in drowned hay might just have found
a shorter channel to oblivion.

Dorianne Laux

JOURNAL ENTRY: APRIL, 1996

The Doctor Dred Radio Active Food Lab is advertised on Saturday morning TV three times during *Crossfire*, a religious show for teens in which the vitriolic host stares into a sea of scared kids and tells them that if they have sex they will die—which is mostly true—and incinerate in hell forever. Also advertised is the *Crash and Smash Set* from Hot Wheels, monsters on miniature motorcycles who are set on a maze of plastic ramps. At every junction, a plastic brick wall. Wound up, the monsters slide at high speeds toward either side of the wall which they crash into before they smash into each other and break apart. A close-up of the aftermath reveals a leg here, an arm there, two alien heads rolling to a kiss amid the rubble. This is called Fun. This is how they play, how they prepare for a short life of sudden death and dismemberment—little dual suicides—the final connection. This is what we feed our children: Fear, annihilation and nuclear food. And yet vestiges of the fantasy persist, *The Ken and Barbie Wedding Set*, complete with a *Playdoh* cake, a boxy house cut in half, a bedroom with a four-poster bed. The Prince and his Princess in tux and gown stare blindly at the white canopy frills, at the infinitesimal stitches in the quilt. They are not allowed the terror of genitals. Though in the living room, in front of the matchbox TV, stretched out on a plastic couch, a pint-sized GI Joe is allowed his silver can of beer, his tiny guns and grenades, his plastic bayonet. More cartoons. More marshmallows in the neon-colored cereals. They eat what we give them; we spoon it into their mouths and they chew on it until their eyes glow.

Amy Klauke-Minato

A HEART FOR DARKNESS

In the movie *To Kill a Mockingbird,* Scout, a nine-year-old girl, and her older brother Jem, 11, are left alone to wander, dream, skip, search, adventure. Scout, with her short hair and overalls, hanging upside-down on the swing, might have been me at that age, claiming the outdoors as I knew it. When I was a kid, most of my non-school time was spent outside, playing running games with the neighbors, napping on the lawn, reading in the old elm tree in the back corner of the yard. Sometimes I'd go visit my friend Jeannie a few blocks away, and return slowly in the quiet dark, holding the sense of the night's power close against my heart.

Outside is where seasons played out their brilliance. In winter, I built snow forts and chewed on icicles, in spring I looked for minuscule fish in the muddy creek, in summer I caught fireflies in the field, and in autumn it was my job to tend the burning leaves in the metal barrel that marked the separation between our yard and the next. I would go out after dinner, the temple-keeper, mesmerized by the flames licking the sides, the ashes that swirled away carrying my wishes to the stars.

As teenagers, my friends and I would make fires and sleep all night on the beach. We'd meet in parks and tell secrets. Nearby cornfields at dusk served as my running track, the familiar rustle of corn and long low horizon marked my place on the land. It seemed I could always run faster and farther in the dark. Whenever things at home got hard, I'd lie alone in the damp grass until the earth had drained away all the stress.

During those years, I would go wilderness camping with small groups of women. Part of that time we would each do a solo camping experience. Although it was scary at first, the power and insight we gained both from being alone and together away from "civilization" was one of the deepest freedoms I have yet experienced. The relationships among our group were based on mutual appreciation and respect. A new kind of community became possible when the old one was left behind.

At age twenty-four, I came out west to be closer to the wilderness I love. Every day, I would walk in the town park at dawn and at dusk to keep in daily touch with the natural world. I would leave any worry I had with the trees. At various times I would repeat a mantra to myself, representing whatever quality in myself I was trying to nurture, *courage, patience, joy.* Sometimes I would focus on an animal that represented a quality I aspired to develop, like the beaver's industriousness, the otter's play, the heron's stillness. Nature afforded a place of meditation that conventional churches never gave me. But it was imperative that I lose myself in thought, that I feel safe in my "temple."

Then, one day while on my walk, I was approached by a naked man yelling obscenities. Another day a car of drunk men followed me, calling out comments. Although part of me felt safer with the dark woods beside me to hide in, I realized that such incidents would be less likely on a well-lit busy street. When a disturbed neighbor began to stalk me, I gave up my walks in the park. I was afraid.

Over the last twenty years the world has whittled away bits of my three sources of strength and solace: solitude, nature, and my relationship with the night. These losses challenge the direction society has taken. We are steeped in fear and man-made culture. To be quiet and alone outside in the dark has become a dangerous activity—especially for a woman.

This theft of our solitude in nature has happened mostly indirectly. The media portrays women alone outside at night being raped and attacked. We women learn that these things really happen. A man hassles us on the street, two follow us home, another hides outside our apartment building, one calls on the phone to say he is watching our house. Slowly the image of the world and our role in it changes. Our trust erodes, we begin to circumscribe our lives. We learn that women are meant to stay at home, not go out alone or without a man at night or to a secluded place ever. . . . *ever.* This is a prison sentence which most of us accept. And if we don't obey and something happens, it is considered our fault because we have strayed from our societal boundaries.

Yet, to me the night continues to be like the reclusive neighbor portrayed in *To Kill a Mockingbird*, Boo Radley, whom everyone fears but who in the end saves the children's lives. Although presented as dangerous and evil, Boo, like the night, offers tremendous richness, support and peace. It is society that has made the dark seem terrible, and keeps us from developing a healthy relationship with it.

I believe the retreat from nature and from the night cripples our spirit. For me, as someone who loves nature so deeply, it severely limits the source of my inspiration. I need the ongoing opportunity to compare a natural system and my feelings in it to the roles I've been assigned within this man-made world. I believe wilderness can bring out the best in all of us.

For that reason, I have chosen to develop self-defense skills, courage, knowledge and to work for societal change. I have decided not to give up on camping, hiking, or walking at night alone. If someone tries to hurt me, I will fight back. Maybe I will be wounded or killed. But that risk is less depressing than the thought of living an atrophied life severed from the beauty and profundity of nature, silence, darkness, and of my own deepest self.

Last night on my night walk I startled a raccoon on a front porch. It stood up and froze, watching my movements to see if I would cause it harm. Slowly it retreated up a nearby tree, but I knew it would be back once I left. I recognized the danger this raccoon faced, searching for sustenance in a neighborhood full of dogs and cars, recognized that its territory, like mine, was being ceaselessly erased. But I also acknowledged the boldness we shared, moving toward what has been denied us, claiming our place in this precarious, imperfect world.

These days, I work with a nature education group. The children we serve tend to have little experience with nature. They are often timid and fearful. Their time with us may be their only outdoors experience, and this qualified by the presence of an adult. How different from my own childhood experiences or those of Scout and Jem. I often wonder if these city-bred children will ever enjoy the time alone in nature that deepened my own thoughts and feelings as a young girl. And if they don't, how will their generation—disconnected from nature, and raised on fear and violence—steer the world on a gentler, healthier path?

Elisavietta Ritchie

SIGHT LINES

Hard to tell, in silhouette
in the shadow of the overpass,
if they are approaching
or going away.

If they are coming toward you,
do you enter, hope they keep
walking past like ordinary
pedestrians on a crowded street.

If they are receding toward
that far arch, will they wait
just beyond, out of your sight,
or run after a bus, or someone else.

Will you, who always thought
you knew your direction, keep on,
turn back, or take the long
way up and over the tracks.

Emily Robertson

GLASS PIPE PRISON

the white boys got him hooked/she thought they was up all night/in broke cars talkin' politics with a little red wine/she woke up mornings/not botherin' tryin' to nudge him back to life/thinkin'/thank–you god/i see the sun/thank–you for the new day/she rose from her dreams/each day/thinkin' she was free/her mind traveled far and wide/but she had never learned to stop at the obvious/so wouldn't have known/her man/her love/was masturbating on the white horse/she didn't know he was collecting glass pipes/lining them up/one by one/he didn't ask her permission/or notify her/that he was building a prison/she remembered the December days/they fried pork chops/smothered potatoes/and made butter biscuits/so how could she hold that same light to face present day?/she found herself/bein' his mentor/his loyal followin' and all/had somehow got trapped within the glass pipe walls/right there on a pretty street/where butterflies dozed on parked cars/she understood guilt by association/but still craved satisfaction from lies/she liked the reassurin' sound of her voice/tellin' friends/yes, i'm alright/her friends weren't around that day/and her voice had nowhere to go/when her love/gave her blue flowered dress/the one she had worn to the audition/considered a good luck symbol/to the dopeman/for a cracked pearl/a bit of broken heaven/crystallized lies/melted to molasses/sucked into his lungs/he came out the bathroom/feelin' like the man/and who was this bitch?/he kept askin' her/what did you do with that dress/the blue flowered one/your rabbit foot?/he said/baby, baby/i wanna see you in it/he made her tear up the apartment lookin' for it/and when it didn't turn up he accused his sister of stealin' it/his high was takin' him there/and it was his intention to drive her crazy/make her think perhaps she was not sane/another betty davis/in whatever happened to baby jane/he wouldn't let her out the house/which is why she overheard his call to a brother named bull/who at the time was supplyin' the whole neighborhood/she heard her man say/did your girl like the dress/what can you give me/i got a leather coat she would look sweet in/so she hid the coat/her leather coat/a gift from a friend/under the sink/but where/she needed to know/where could she go/to hide/in his glass pipe prison/

Sharon Doubiago

OUTLAW

1.

Don't shoot, I've
eaten this country alive

Your hard male body, like a road, I drove
your famous miles, backs of vans
low on backseats

The states grow out of me now
The borders are my skin
The fatal flag flies, tattooed
between my hips

The hum of my motor
blends with the thump of little bodies
and the static rockbeat
of the radio

and I am gone
like the semen you spilt to the ground
when you fantasized me a whore
and then would not love me
for fear I was a whore

2.

Everyone was looking for me
I was always right here
a mute piece of music
a deep down motion
running through your blood

Don't shoot
In the windows of all your homes
my face is printed
where I pressed it to the glass

she

who robbed her father's banks

3.

Crowds on the streets at night looking for me
But I was caught
in the dancer's grace of apple trees
in a cold country
I never lived before

Don't shoot, who
could recognize me now?
There's a dead man
hanging
in the middle of my forehead
His cold charred body
emerges
from my cunt and anus
My mouth expels
a new country

4.

And so I walked away in my rich white skin
while you scattered all your parts to the wind

I picked up your hand
without fingers
by the winter waters

and placed it on my breasts

you were still warm
I called your name
You did not answer

So I'm gone
like the semen you spilt on the ground
when you wanted me a whore

and then could not love me
for fear I was a whore

5.

I am a woman
a traveler back and forth

I joined the army
traveling back and forth
across the continent

the sun coming up
the sun going down
the stars planted in their routes

the dancer's grace of apple trees
in a cold country
I never lived before

I learned constellations, windrows
rotations of farmers' land
food for the people
and the ache of you

the fucking ache of you

What does it take
to communicate?
The words burnt deep in my flesh

burn a gory road before me
the only escape

6.

Everyone was looking for me
I was always right here

Once I camped in a national park
with a caravan of retired people
At night inside their little campers
their blue phosphorescent lights
served me up for dinner, a cold burn

this is your daughter
this is your daughter

Everyone
was afraid
I was
their daughter

7.

I am the woman alone on the road at night
you catch in your headlights
Afraid, you do not stop

I walk in the middle of the world
with a child at each side
another tied in a scarf on my back

Tonight we will sleep in a cold open field
I will lay my hands on its heart

I will blanket them with pine needles
I will hear the screech and groan of wagon wheels
I will pull dead Indians from the soil

I will be thankful I have not house nor land
I will be thankful I have no money

I am a woman
I walk in the middle of the world
I follow the cross of the gypsy trail
over the world and back

8.

I went down to the bottom of the mountains
I went down to the bottom of the sea in your scrotum
I rode out the dark untried eggs

I saw the body and soul are one
I saw when the body fragments
so does the soul

I saw that in death our parts
are strewn and scattered

piece of flesh, piece of soul

and our tortured lament
is our parts
crying to one another
across the ever-widening
abyss

9.

I am only a mother
trying to piece together
a child

10.

I am a woman
a traveler back and forth

When I knelt to your groin the first time
and took you in my mouth
I felt the fish beat
for the cold pull
of a distant sea

and when I took you in my mouth
I was the moon receiving
your wondrous light

now I am scattered like stars
you spilt
on the ground

11.

I was held down

My clitoris was cut out
with the broken neck of a bottle
and thrown in the dirt

I am your clitoris
singing in the throats of little sparrows

I was held down

My fetus was cut out
and thrown into the sewer

I am your daughter
I was saved by the water
that threw me on the shore
I was raised by wolves
I belong to No Man's Land

I was held down

My breasts were cut off
and thrown in the Rockies
I tattooed on my scars
a heart with an arrow
plunged all the way through

I am your breasts
thrust up as the Rockies
though arrowheads, mining shafts
and mineral hot springs
are lost deep in my folds

I am gone
into the dark activity beneath your skin
and come up again through you
the caves of history
the boy becoming king
dreams

I am a woman
a traveler back and forth
I belong to No Man's Land
who hung my torso
from every post

and filled all my small holes
with rocks

12.

I hold my womb in my hands
its ever-living population
I will never have children
They must rise in me

The Present Living Body

13.

I made love to a woman in the Rockies
A prayer in the middle of the world
We rolled back and forth
across the native soil
the flesh of Pocahontas
while under us
old gods jacked off
embarrassed

14.

My crimes are many
I loved a Mojave boy
and dreamed every night
I impregnated him

I am a streetwalker
I lie down with all of you
I take you in my body
The more you fuck me
the less you know me

I am the 9 million witches
you burned at the stake
Now I am back, bounding over the hills I move
into every house
I change my clothes in each one
I am your daughter

I am every furtive fantasy
you've ever had
I am your left hand

15.

I am the lissome young girl
who captivated the gaze
of all those who saw me

You were clenched and breathless
as we went down
and I took you
deep inside

many ghosts were colored lights
the aurora borealis
raining, tumbling, roaring
chasing years across the sky

When I took you in my mouth
I was the moon
receiving the light
that lit our tent
and morning that waited
at the end of the world

now I am crazy Jane
I will leap from my grave
when you walk by

I vanished long ago

gone like semen spilt on the ground
gone like last year's wild roses

like the hot stars you carry in your little sacks
like the hot stars trailing from my mouth

gone like morning at the end of the world

like the sun risen half way to noon
and then falling back to dawn

John R. Campbell

VULNERABILITY AND LOVE

Compared with Love, Your Triune Law,
All the inexorable stars are anarchists:
Yet they are bound by Love and Love is infinitely free.

Minds cannot understand, nor systems imitate
The scope of such simplicity.
—Thomas Merton

Entering the expansive light of the Klamath Basin, it's hard to conceive of shadow as overwhelming. Here the literal shadows don't oppress. Instead, they add interest, chiaroscuro variation, and depth to the open range. But there are figurative shadows as well, more encompassing than mountains or clouds, that can rise steadily and cover the land.

I first sensed a presence at the Sprague River, just up from Chiloquin. Stopping to fish, I noticed a beaver plying the current. I only glimpsed its tail, but it was so utterly flat and black against the complexity of light on the water that it articulated a gap. Such gaps open, briefly, to the void.

At first the shadow falls selectively, in shards and fragments; it falls on debris. Between the road and the river is the usual trash, the snuff cans, the giant drink cups, the packaging of lures and hooks, and something more—half a deer skull, the cranium lit like a cracked moon, and an intact backbone and pelvis, still pinkish in places, lying open to the world like a valentine. As the Klamath Indians fish on their dissolved reservation for spring trout, and as the buildings out on Modoc Point continue to crumble, I wonder at humans casting other humans aside, as if they were mere casualties of momentum. I remember the coprolites, the human feces found in Oregon desert caves, preserved in the dry air for 9500 years. They contain evidence of wild onion, sego lily, wild rose seeds, prickly pear cactus, wild cherry, and sunflower. They contain the hair, bones, or shells of antelope, of rodents, of freshwater shellfish and crayfish. They contain evidence of parasites, and of tule reeds gnawed to extract the sparse nutrients. In the ancient debris is the proof, of ingenuity, intimacy, perseverance, and suffering. What do we value? What do we toss aside? What will future peoples learn when they examine our debris?

Now the day is waning, and the shadow descends on all the public and the private spaces. In the shallows at Hagglestein Park, hovering terns look straight down into the water. Their shadows might eliminate the glare, revealing the fingerlings beneath, so that the birds might dive. They simply want something to offer their young on the flotsam nests nearby. I know my task is to emulate them, to access what Thomas Merton calls "the scope of such simplicity," to dismantle my metaphors in order to make use, as the birds do, of both shadow and debris. My task is to submit to the rusting barrels in the roadside ditch, to the RV park filled with severed willows. But something in me resists and resists, and the shadow assumes new forms, images both strange and necessary.

When dusk comes on, I find myself at Veteran's Park on the small lake backed up by the Klamath River dam. I'm as flat and complacent as the water, as the unseen dam. A mix of wild and domestic geese dot the pond, and overhead, a few birds fly the disappeared river corridor. Pelicans float near shore, red knobs on their bills. A duck drops his wings to an inverted U and lands out of light's range. On the parking lot, two male mallards are humping and pecking a female. How can I call them merciless, except in the purest sense of the word, when they have no need for mercy?

The falling night envelopes me in a sad privacy. All around the signs of municipal pride darken: the spindly tree, the new landscaping, the empty information booth. The cars on the highway ramp overhead only serve to enhance my anonymity, the smattering of lights on the far shore and the radio towers blinking, to seed my alienation. When a late pelican arrives, gliding in the final glimmer of sky on water, its body seems suddenly transparent.

Last night I drove into the cliffs above Upper Klamath Lake. I was bound, in the rain, for an overlook where I intended to sleep. When I arrived at the spot, though, I was surprised to find a white sedan parked there, its windows clouded, its engine idling. Or perhaps I wasn't surprised at all.

Continuing up the road, mice scampering in my headlights, I found another pull-off, and I killed the engine, listening to the rain and pondering the darkness over the lake. If the shadow exists at peace with itself, if there is a calm in the absolute blackness over water, it is far apart from me. It's autonomous, like the scaups and the gorgeous pintails still swimming in my memory. Like the night heron's croak or the cormorant's almost fluorescent orange facial skin, it defies my expectations as a matter of course. But I felt closer, somehow, as if I occupied the edge of that calm, never quite at home there, but silent in awe of its incomprehensible core. All night I kept vigil as the squalls arrived and moved on, as the occasional Southern Pacific freight rumbled below.

Images kept flooding my eyes. Canada goslings, golden on the sides of their faces and necks, jumbled up behind an adult. Weathered pornography stashed beneath some sage. Ubiquitous egrets, silent as snow. Piles of railroad ties, black and vivid, on an embankment along the tracks. I thought of how we walk through a waking dream, projecting our psyches everywhere, physically building crude representations on the land. Some are so obvious we may not notice them; I remembered a black sailboat, with a yellow sail, named "Panic." I remembered phallic silos. I thought of the animal features of cars: slits, eyes, fins, and haunches.

Do we wish to render the world as a model of mind? There are tangled freeways and convoluted ramps. There are books, there is music, invisible on the airwaves. Or do we want to model the body, badly because we know it so little? There are malls; there are airports; there are townships that sprawl. Maybe we really wish to model the very act of wishing, our desire. So we arrive anxious at movie houses, or we turn around sullenly on streets that dead-end at the edge of the endless sage.

But there is something more. The animals and the land are out there, accepting our projections, but at the same time asserting an autonomy that haunts. They are more vast than any of our psychic monuments. They comprise the ground against which our fabricated figures stand.

Now, at dawn, a bald eagle drifts over the lake. A few Cascade peaks shine through the loosening front, their snow pastel in the eastern light. In a little clearing I notice some filthy white fur: two domestic rabbits lie drenched and dead, their eyes missing, their ears frayed. The shadow is omnipresent, as neutral and recurrent as morning. As I drive down the mountain, quail troop into the manzanita, and the smell of diesel drifts up from the highway below. On the radio, the country songs are all plaintive, about love.

Why do I so often find myself in wild and forlorn places? I ask myself this small question as the Basin is brushed by rain. Certainly

I'm not always comforted here, where vast clouds and empty spaces sweep the human away. Where tans deepen to blues so dark as to seem irredeemable. Where the barns are decrepit, and the horses practice their version of Stoicism, backs to the wind. They're only animals, like us, bred to suffer well.

Out on the road, far from home, loneliness can settle in as easily as the rain. The highway itself is slight and tenuous. The ramshackle churches can't reassure me, nor can the county sheriff in his steady car.

But near Henley today there's a brightly painted school. The ballfield there is bristling with young girls playing softball, oblivious to the drizzle, raised amidst the vastness they've either absorbed or learned to ignore. Their American tenacity touches me—what need produces these geometries in the wild.

Baseball in the tamed fields: I remember my own upbringing, on the prairie converted to houses and malls. I remember a time when light was more infused with my fears than darkness. In a suburb northwest of Chicago, I played in rich, glacially-deposited soil, strange to my own native countryside. Across the street from our house was an empty field. I shouldn't say empty—it was planted in bluegrass, uniform except for the token cornpatch back by an unused barn. Magnus Farm, once agricultural, had been converted to a geriatric home, and the fields were the *grounds*, I guess, insulating the frail bodies from our everyday commerce. As a kid I'd sometimes squint to see if a crone might be making her way from the far brick building, but I never did see her coming. We children ran out there willingly, filling the void with our chatter and derisive shouts. The field, rimmed in osage orange trees, was a theater in which our baseball dramas unfolded, in which our frail kites were somehow held in the sky.

Even today when I travel, Magnus Field underlies any field I might encounter. And when I dream of the wild, Magnus Field is the ground for my dream. Sometimes the field is a shallow sea teeming with plankton. Sometimes wolves or geese dot the plain. When my remote ancestors first emerged from the trees, lighting their plains with fires, they must have known this sense of an adorned landscape, where space and time are mottled with animal life. They must have shivered, as I have, at the storms' ozone approaching across the fields. But their world, a pattern of animal, plant, mineral, and water influences, was so complex as to demand mythological understanding. Mine, the intricacies of bluegrass notwithstanding, was so simplified that it demanded a mythology to *fill it in*. And even as I've moved off to fill the space in my travels and in my dreams, developers have filled it in with reality: condominiums and homes.

Indeed, my whole childhood was marked by the development of the fields and woods all around my house. The old layers of land went under, replaced inevitably by the simple artifice of asphalt and lawns. So my impulse now is to redeem the land, to allow the ground to return to some former, richer state. But the developer's impulse is to redeem the land as well, to progress the ground into some future, richer state. Our ethics, emphasis, and economics obviously differ, but our underlying narratives are remarkably alike. As much as I'd like to separate myself from the anonymous capitalists who emptied my field and then paved it over, I can't. We all carry with us a barely tangible sense of permanent loss—it's just that my developers were an extra step removed from the earthly paradise of Eden, and an extra step closer to the heavenly paradise beyond.

But let me tell you a story. As a young teen, I liked to sneak out at night and roam the fields and the remnant patches of woods. One night I rendezvoused with a girl at Magnus Field. I wanted her as an animal, wanted her to fill that empty field. She actually loved me, and I loved her, too, in a complex adolescent way. She lived on the opposite side of the field from me; we sometimes met in the middle, though she whispered in fear of her mother who might find out.

Anyway, there we were, on a summer's night. I'll admit to being interested in more than just kissing. In coaxing this girl to roll with me in an empty field, I simulated the night sky above: planets rolled, as if alive, with their compliant moons, and double stars revolved around each other endlessly. Every urge is natural. And this is what I told her.

But the countenance of her mother must have also scowled somewhere in the constellations, because my would-be lover was aloof, stiff and shy. Even sitting on the ground made her nervous. She said her mother checked for grass stains; stains of any kind were abhorrent in her mother's house.

Still, we were young animals then, abandoned to clumsy knowing. So it happened that she slid her pants down to her knees. And that I had my pants at half-mast as well. But just as we began to thrill at each other's wild indifference, to feel the earth seep up in our bones, we heard a shuffling of skirts in the dark. A figure emerged, gaunt, leaning on a cane. She came just close enough that I could see her aged face, pale and long, the mouth and eyes wide.

Looking back, I can see our humiliation hanging in the air like vapor. I can feel the turbulence as the old woman's world crumbled around her. I can sense confusion filling the air to the point of condensation, and I can feel the hot dew on the grass. Magnus Field was always corrupted ground; it simply required periodic rituals like this one to keep it empty and foul. Who wouldn't, if they could turn a profit from it, build decent homes atop this dirt? Shame was the urge that brought the bulldozers and the Cats to scour the earth. Leveling that field, scraping it down to clean and even soil: that was a service to all of us.

Shortly after that night, the city changed its street lamps from the old blue-purple to the new vapor lights. A ghastly amber glare flooded the world, and trees grew all night under the street lamps. Even Magnus Field was affected by the new brightness, its fringes lit, caught naked in the smallest hours. Needless to say, I stopped sneaking out at night. I broke up with my girlfriend and began reading Dostoyevsky. Every space became interior space, and rooms soon filled the fields.

Elizabeth Claman

KENEL, SOUTH DAKOTA

In the Lakota's land, the scrub brush hills and valleys, I think of Wounded Knee; Black Elk's descriptions of the white "wasichu" soldiers—a menacing horde. From a bluff I see a lake dotted with speed boats and windsurfers. Curious, I drive down and discover it's a reservoir. The wind races patterns across its surface. Somehow incongruous, on its banks I find a wooden plaque which reads,

"When the Oak Dam was built, making a 200 mile lake of the Missouri River between Bismark and Pierre, the Kenel cemetery had to be moved. These names are from the graves, dating from the 1800s, which could not be moved:

JOSEPH AFRAID OF EAGLE
JEROME BEAR FACE
MATTHEW BLACK HAT
LEO BLUE SPOTTED
MOSES BRAVE
GERTRUDE KILLS TWO
CLARA OMAHA
ADELINA CROW FEATHER
BEDA SMELL THE BEAR
MARIUS FIRE HEART
JOHN AFRAID OF NOTHING
MARIE FAT BELLY
JACOB BLUE IRON
ALMA BOX DREAM
MARIE MANY WOUNDS
ROSE CHARGING THUNDER
AEGIDIUS WAMBLWOKAPI
REGINA THIEF
BARNABAS CHASE FIRST
MARY WALKING ELK."

D. M. Wallace

THE STORM BEFORE THE STORM

All day dark clouds have teemed
and separated, threatening rain.
I've moved through it smoothly
in my black dress, holding back
outbursts. Sexual politics divide
my will, my breath makes s's
behind my teeth, my lips move
diplomatic, sweet, impure.

I get worked like so much putty,
but ride home spitting *pitiable*
bastard, poor fool, pure shit.
I scream along the bike path unlaced,
my soul ragged and unwhole,
my thoughts unwholesome.

I come through the door dripping
sweat, still unable to break.
My spine grows taut like a
hanging tree hung with someone
in darkness, diving into the void.

My child's cry comes in jagged
thrusts, a sound like machine gun
fire. He growls like a dog,
screwing his head into the bed.

First clap of thunder he runs
for me, presses his forehead into
mine, a blessing for the both
of us, our tears falling old
as these clouds that finally
give out.

Joseph Millar

TWENTIETH-CENTURY LANDSCAPES

We are down on our knees
in the cement vault under Harrison Street
listening to the big cable
slither toward us through the pipes.
All day the long trucks
have unloaded their pallets of steel
onto the cracked asphalt behind us,
while the rain scatters on the walls
of the Granny Goose Potato Chip Factory
and the line crew silently tabulates
the minutes of overtime, slowly collecting
the pull-ropes and fish-tapes
and coiling them into the truckbed.

Most of us are thankful. Soon
this cable will be in and we can go home
traveling speechless and half awake
back through West Oakland, past
the stained doors of the transmission shop
on Cypress Avenue and the blotched facade
of St. Vincent de Paul's, the ripped
tarp flapping across its window
like a forgotten angel and the cracked tiles
of the Chinese movies shining in the rain.

In our homes we will eat
cheeseburgers and new potatoes
while the news channel flickers
with the sound turned low
over fluid tableaus of athletes
bathed in million-dollar sweat
and the wrecked landscapes of Bosnia
freezing behind barbed wire.
We watch them interview the darkhaired women
speaking in fractured bursts, hands
fluttering away from their breasts
like winter sparrows startled
by the voices rising into the sharp air
from mass graves under the snow.

It's a hard war to figure out.
Fascism presses its humped shadow down
across shattered bridges and colonnades
from the Sixteenth Century,
and into the steep valleys
bristling with landmines. Arabic fountains
blister away, riddled with shrapnel
under charred minarets, the ruined
mosaics and upraised palm
of the Heretic Christ
bulldozed flat in the dust.

Why don't we do something, some of us
wonder, as the cameras slide easily back
over the smooth bodies of Cadillacs
and white people vacationing in Jamaica.
But something wants us to go to sleep.
This morning, joking in the Parts Line
with our clipboards full of work orders,
the wire spools stacked in the doorway
waiting to be counted and the ladders
clattering down onto the gravel,
the foreman told me his stock options
earned an extra four grand this year.
Another month like this last one, he says,
and we can take the kids to Disneyland.

Probably it's daylight
in Bosnia by now. Unshaven men
keep lowering their eyes, shifting in the cold
from one foot to another and refusing
to look into the cameras.
The corporation the President works for
is wide awake, breaking down the costs
of the Election Campaign and tomorrow
we'll be back under the street,
dreaming of overtime and talking baseball,
while history smolders
in the Balkan hills
and the cleansed human cinders
float through the dawn
still partly on fire in the wind.

Ellyn Bache

THE VALUE OF KINDNESS

Late the night of her fifty-third birthday, Cora Russ put on a dark shirt and trousers and stealthily began raking pine straw from her neighbor's yard. Earlier she'd eaten tempura shrimp at a Japanese restaurant with her husband, Seth, who gave her a bottle of expensive cologne—Estee Lauder's "Beautiful"—and her son Jason, a senior in high school, who presented her with a pair of earrings. After they went home, Seth watched updates on Operation Desert Shield until he fell asleep on the couch, and Jason did homework while talking on the phone to his girlfriend. Around midnight, Jason finally went to bed.

The Rutherfords, whose yard Cora was raking, had small children and no time for gardening. The tall pines which dotted their property had begun to shed yellowed needles a month ago, and now the pine straw was solid, smothering the grass. Under her dark clothes, Cora broke a sweat which enabled her to work with feverish energy. It was one of those almost-balmy Southern nights that persisted even into late fall, moonless and soft. The Rutherford house was dark. Cora judged that even if they weren't sleeping, they wouldn't notice her. If they did, would they have her arrested? She wasn't sure it mattered. When Cora was a child she thought anyone over a certain age deserved to die and probably wanted to. She couldn't imagine the passion to live persisting in a soft, wrinkled body. She assumed anyone so ugly would be too embarrassed to want to carry on. Now she reasoned that if she intended to live out her fifty-third year, she might as well be useful. Besides, what could she be arrested for? Trespassing? It wasn't as if she were stealing. She raked the pine straw into a neat pile at the end of the yard, feeling like Robin Hood. When she was finished she went back into her house and woke Seth to tell him it was time to go to bed.

"Where've you been?" he yawned.

"Out walking. I was restless."

"Looks more like you were running."

"A little."

He grinned sleepily. "Worried about getting old? Trying to keep in shape?" Seth owned a successful employment agency which allowed him time to work out at a health club and run three miles a day. When Cora had first met him, he was in the Army training troops to go to Vietnam, his body hard and uniformly tan, lighter on the belly, far more beautiful than her own. Now, even with activity, his muscles had lost some of their tone and his skin had grown mottled with tiny dark spots—not moles or freckles so much as the ravages of middle age—which reminded Cora, especially now, of her oldness.

The hour of raking hit her all at once after she undressed, leaving her bone-weary under a hot shower. Because of her birthday, Seth would make love to her when she got out. Unnecessary, she wanted to say. And wanted to discuss, too, other matters of concern now that she was belatedly menopausal. If it's not wet, don't touch it. Make it wet first. Then. Had there been some other man, some other life, she might have managed this, but divulging such privacies to Seth after twenty-three years of marriage was as unthinkable as dyeing her hair orange or strutting naked through the house. In any case, there was no discussing the crux of it—that though she genuinely cared for him, believed he was the only man she could have lived with this long and want to continue the arrangement, even so, for the moment she would just as soon not be touched at all.

"You still have nice legs for an old lady," he whispered as she got into bed, making her feel doubly evil for the clinical and unflattering statements she knew would occupy her as they touched: He's pumping my breast as if it were a cow's udder. He's latching onto the nipple like a baby nursing. As if "he" had no name. As if she were writing journal entries or a book.

The next day her arms were sore from raking, stippled deep inside with little points of fire. Were the neighbors up yet? Had they examined the yard and been puzzled, or did they know perfectly well why the raking had been done and by whom? She dressed for work carefully. Too big-boned for elegance, she'd opted years ago for formidability. She bought severe, expensive suits and good jewelry. She reasoned that these helped stave off the irate husbands who sometimes came looking for their spouses at the domestic violence center she administered. The truth was, the living quarters of the shelter were on the other side of a deliberate maze of hallways that led from the front offices, and the security system was so elaborate that the women were safe even without Cora's intervention. She herself spent most of her time on the phone or at meetings except when she deemed it wise to give a tour of the shelter to assure continued funding.

She was greeted by Shirley Coleman, the shelter's manager, herself once a battered wife who'd taken her two children and left—a large vivacious black woman, or "woman of color" as Shirley put it; she never used the term black. Shirley's office was off the shelter's main hall, where she greeted each newcomer with such open arms that briefly, even if they came with bruises or broken limbs, she engulfed them, comforted them, convinced them there were possibilities.

"Somebody wanting to give us a couch and chair," Shirley said, hanging up the phone as Cora entered. "She didn't seem to care when I said we'd have to look at it first, so maybe it'll be okay."

"Ever the optimist," Cora replied. They had calculated that forty percent of their would-be contributions were offered not as charity but in hopes that someone would cart away useless junk. "I'll have Pauline check it out—maybe this morning." Cora generally didn't send volunteers on errands that might require tact, but Pauline was one of several who'd served the shelter so long and with such devotion that if Cora had let them do all they offered, she would hardly have had to work full-time herself. She would have, of course. She didn't trust anyone who stayed home too much after their children reached a certain age. She abhorred the thought of falling into the dependent, narrow lives of women protected and supported by men, playing tennis, shopping too much, waking one day to discover with shock and outrage that they were widowed or divorced or deemed, in some other way, unnecessary.

"Better save the furniture and let Pauline cover the phone this morning," Shirley said. "Don't forget that brunch."

"The medical auxiliary." Usually it was lunch, or with men's groups, dinner. They could almost always count on their presentation convincing the group in question to put the shelter on its charities list. "I should have known when I saw you wearing shoes," Cora said.

"Miserable uncomfortable shoes, too."

As a concession to the occasion, Shirley had on modest black leather heels instead of the white canvas flats she normally claimed were all her wide feet could endure. The rest of her outfit consisted of her usual comfortable elastic-waist skirt and a cheap sweater—not, this morning, in her accustomed hot pinks or neon golds or fluorescent limes—"to look a little cheerful, you know?" The colors delighted the children and cheered the women—including, often, Cora, who at those times wished she had Shirley's willingness not to dress for success. Today Shirley's blouse was ordinary red, conservative compared to the neons, and topped with a string of pearls that might have come from the dollar store.

The medical auxiliary, when they arrived and confronted it, was dressed in pale silks or muted harvest colors, which daunted Shirley not at all. Their usual plan for these occasions was to have Cora make introductions and brief remarks and let Shirley do most of the speaking. As Shirley bluntly put it, "The ladies always like to see a real, ex-battered wife."

In any case, Cora couldn't concentrate. Looking at the well-dressed well-fed audience, many of whom she knew from around the neighborhood, what she wanted most was to confess: "Last night at midnight I dressed in dark clothes like a robber and went out to rake the ratty pine straw off the Rutherford's lawn." It was all she could do to suppress this urge and introduce Shirley and sit back down.

Even on Cora's more eloquent days, it was Shirley's manner rather than Cora's that generally drew the audience's sympathy and elicited the donation. Shirley was earnest, she was ebullient, she was calm and sure. "What you got to realize is, the time she's most at risk is right now with the holidays coming up. Or if it would be her birthday. He don't want her to have no good memories."

"Don't want her" and "no good memories." Shirley could just as easily say "doesn't want" and "any memories"—Cora had heard her do so. In and out of the less grammatical cadence, depending on the audience. Unselfconsciously, working almost from instinct—survival instinct?—that told her one audience would respond better to standard diction, another to the more exotic, ethnic mode of speech.

"What sort of women come to the shelter?" someone asked. "All kinds? Or mainly of a certain income level?" By which she meant: white women or just black?

"Most middle class white women, if they have some money, they don't come to the shelter—they get on a plane and take a three week vacation," Shirley said. Laughter. "Not that the trip solves the problem. But for women of color—they don't have the choice. We get mostly women of color."

One by one, Shirley slipped off her heels and stood behind the podium with her wide feet naked on the tiled floor. The audience was rapt. "What he does first is, he isolates her. If she wants to go out with friends, he makes her feel bad. He says, 'You rather be with them than with me.' He criticizes her family. A lot of times, he won't lay a hand on her until he's got her cut off from everybody. Until all she's got to depend on is him." She. When asked, Shirley told her own story in a detached, pleasant tone. So mild, such a sweet pulp. How had she escaped bitterness when her ex-husband had broken her nose, shattered her jaw? Cora tried to imagine rising from unspeakable horror, going back to show others the way. She'd never known unspeakable horrors, of course; indeed, horrors of any kind. Having not, how could she be sure she'd have the strength to escape them?

"Your yard looks terrific," Cora said to Peggy Rutherford, her heart thrumming in her throat, blood rushing through her ears. "When did you rake it?"

"You won't believe it, but we didn't. We woke up one morning and here it was." She removed the hand that was pushing her toddler on the swing and made a quick sweep around the lawn and toward the pile of pine straw. "Overnight. It was bizarre." The swing glided back and Peggy propelled it forward by pushing the middle of her child's spine. In jeans, she seemed tiny, too small to have three young children. "We don't have the faintest idea who did it. Some Good Samaritan. The phantom gardener."

"Well, I wish he'd come prune my roses." A double lie. Pruning bushes was one of the pleasures of Cora's warm winter days.

"It's scary, in a way. Suppose he'd had—I don't know... less benign motives?"

Had her motives been benign? Perhaps not. Cora considered. "A little scary, yes."

Seth had taught one of his all-day job-hunting seminars and now was sprawled across the couch in the family room, beer in hand, not drinking. The TV beamed out interviews with troops assigned to the Saudi desert since August, eating Thanksgiving dinner, sounding homesick and bored. "They ought to get in there and be done with it," he said. "You'd think they'd have learned something from Vietnam."

"What's this, War 101?" asked Jason, coming into the room.

"The voice of experience, son," Seth replied.

"Right. The aging but venerable veteran." Jason folded himself into a heap on the floor.

"With the emphasis on venerable," Seth told him.

Seth had been sent to Vietnam when he and Cora were married less than a year, to a job supervising a mine sweep along a road where dozens of people had been killed. She never knew, until Jason asked his father if he'd ever seen anyone die, that a trooper had once had his legs blown off by a mine they missed, and that Seth had held him while they waited for the Medivac helicopter. "All you can guard against is bleeding and shock," Seth had explained. To the injured soldier he had crooned, over and over again, "Everything is well under control here. Everything is well under control." And when the trooper lost consciousness and his breath rattled, Seth held him closer, did not let go until the breathing stopped.

"Did it make you sick?" Jason had asked.

"You think you'll be sick before it happens," Seth replied. "But when it does, you aren't. You just do what you have to."

After that Seth's unit cut fatalities on that road eighty percent. Later, his first months back home, he startled at every car backfire, every sudden noise. A quick tensing of muscles before he caught himself, hardly visible, so subtle that Cora wouldn't have known unless she was touching him (which she often was in those days) and felt his fright resonate inside her skin.

A year later Seth resigned his commission because he saw a series of desk jobs in his military future. After a year with an employment agency, he decided to start his own, specializing in jobs for other ex-military. But Cora sometimes thought he missed the intensity of Vietnam even now. It seemed he'd had some personal thing to prove there, and that he had—for which she rather envied him.

Ever since, he'd hated the way Vietnam was perceived. "You'd think every third guy who went over there ended up homeless," he complained, resentful of the media claims that so many men came back with emotional scars. He preached to Jason that we would have won, no question, if we'd gone in with proper force. And Jason, when he was younger, had been infected with Seth's enthusiasm, had spent days running around the yard shooting toy M-16's at the enemy. Now Seth hoped for a quick war of mastery in the Persian Gulf to atone for the perceived shame of the other. He envisioned handsome statues to atone for the Vietnam Memorial, which he called "nothing but a wailing wall." He watched the updates on television every night, irritably waiting for action.

"Here. Sit," he said, patting the couch next to him. Cora did. He slung an arm around her and set his untouched beer on the end table. Lately he complained of headaches from even a beer or two, when years ago he'd prided himself on being able to consume almost any amount, in any combination, and still get to work on time the next day.

"You look beat, Dad," Jason observed, studying him.

"Warding off women wears you out," Seth said. "You know how those seminars are. Those employment agency groupies."

"Babes, huh?" Jason asked.

"There are no employment agency groupies, son," Cora said, slipping out from Seth's arm, feigning annoyance. Then the phone rang and Jason bounded out to get it, ungainly as a large dog.

"Sure, go ahead and talk about other women," Cora said with exaggerated petulance, noting the exhausted slash of white along Seth's cheekbones, across the bridge of his nose. "But keep in mind that I'm likely to get up some night while you're sound asleep, and get a giant carving knife, and cut off your wang."

He leaned against her, reviving a little, whispering in her ear: "It'd take a giant carving knife, too."

At her desk, explaining to two young volunteers how to do a bulk mailing, she was burning up, turning crimson, yearning for escape. The hot flashes had been brief at first, pulses of heat beamed from her neck into her face, lasting no more than a second or two. So this is it, she'd thought, wondering what all the uproar was about. Now she babbled on in front of two earnest thirty-year-olds while heated coils glowed inside her chest, up her earlobes, through her skin, casting off some horrid inner fire. Thirty seconds, a minute. Any instant she might ignite, making the volunteers party to the crisis they so desired.

"So you sort them according to zip code, and then depending on how many of each category there are?" one of them repeated.

"Yes." Sweat broke out along her upper lip, down her neck. Visible, surely. "Use the conference table if you want to. Put them in separate piles. There's plenty of room."

In a minute she'd be cold. A ridiculous business. And unnecessary, her doctor had insisted. Unasked, cornering her when she went in with flu, he'd said, "What you need is hormones. Not only will they stop the hot flashes, they'll also protect you from heart attack and osteoporosis."

"What about hormones causing uterine cancer? Or cervical? I know I read something about it."

"Where? In some women's magazine?" Oh, snide now, disapproving. "Even if you do get cancer, it's the easiest kind to cure."

"I don't believe you're actually saying that. Advocating getting cancer!"

Not even a grin. "Usually all that's required is surgery."

"All?"

"We're finding the benefits far outweigh the risks. You really have no choice."

No choice! She didn't mention two grandmothers who'd survived into their eighties without hormones. She thanked him and said she'd think about it.

"Think about it soon, Cora." His voice was grave and dramatic, condescending, as if she were too stupid to understand what was being offered.

Whenever Seth went to an evening meeting, Jason camped out on the family room floor. Tonight he held the TV remote in his hand, switching channels every few seconds in hopes of finding a certain video on MTV or VH-1. He had a violent hunger for one song and one song only, almost an anger. Cora did the dishes, straightened up. At nine o'clock Jason turned the sound to mute and called Leah, his girlfriend. They spoke to each other every night. Before his senior year he'd hardly dated, and now he seemed consumed.

Wandering upstairs to give him privacy, she felt restless, in need of activity. She stripped the sheets from her bed and fetched new ones. Jason's laugh drifted up the stairs—a short, clipped guffaw. What did he and Leah talk about? In school they exchanged lengthy notes which covered most everything—or rather, Jason received notes which Leah wrote. Instead of discarding them or folding them up and tucking them away, Jason left them on his desk or the bathroom counter—the most public places—as if to be sure Cora read them, which she did.

They were oddly sweet, which made Cora like the girl, whom she'd met several times and thought unextraordinary. *I really respect your dedication to running* (during cross-country season). *It's nice to see someone who really cares about studying* (which was news to Cora). Leah's kindnesses made Jason kind in turn. But now. Lately. *What do you want to do Friday night? I know what you really want to do, but what we actually will do is another story.*

She wasn't sure she wanted to be party to this. Not long ago, on the kitchen phone with Cora in plain sight, Jason had said to a male friend, "I'll give her a little time if she wants it. I'll let her decide by herself." And Cora had been relieved. But recently, to that same friend, it was "Christmas vacation, probably. New Year's Eve for sure."

She smoothed the clean sheets onto her bed and rearranged the comforter, then wandered into Jason's room. There were no notes in sight tonight, just scattered shoes and laundry. Cora stripped the soiled linens, brought in new ones. The sound on the TV switched on suddenly, blaring. Rich guitar music, a gravelly male voice singing indecipherable lyrics. In her own wanting days there'd been no videos, only small records which she bought and played over and over again until the grooves wore down and the sound grew foggy. By then Cora was sated, bloated, as if she'd eaten too much sugar. She might have told Jason there'd be many things he'd hunger for, many things he'd get. She might have said it wasn't altogether a pleasant thing, having all you wanted of a thing, wearing out your need.

She shoved his bed out from the wall to make fitting the corners easier. Underneath it was a J.C. Penney catalog turned to a page of slender models in underpants and bras. An old towel beside it had been crumpled into a sticky ball—what in her own youth her brother had crudely termed a come cloth. She carried it to the laundry room, vaguely disgusted.

The week before Christmas, the shelter was packed. "It's like I told you—she don't leave until her children are out of school," Shirley explained to the busy volunteers. "She always thinks of everybody else first."

The latest arrival was Kenya Washington, eighteen years old, who gave lie to Shirley's theory by having no children in school, only a two-year-old daughter, a month-old baby, and a badly bruised chin. Her husband showed up outside Cora's office an hour after she arrived. Cora said no, his wife wasn't anywhere nearby, she couldn't say where she'd been sent, it was useless to ask.

"I know you got her here," Howard Washington replied, patient, almost respectful, standing close to the intercom on the porch. "If unknown person comes on premises," a sign on the shelter wall read, "please call 911 or push panic button"—an alarm connected directly to the police station. It hadn't come to that yet. "I'm gonna find her," Howard Washington said, brushing a hand across the top of his tall box haircut, perching himself on the porch railing. "I got time."

So Cora called the police and Howard Washington, seeing the cruiser turn onto the block, quickly disappeared. In such cases, when a husband might be too persistent and the shelter too vulnerable, the wife was whisked to a safe house in the community until her man cooled off. Cora consulted with Shirley, who instructed the volunteers to begin making calls.

After half an hour, they were still coming up empty. Most of the people they relied on were away for the holidays or busy with guests. "I'll take her for a day or two if I have to," Cora whispered to Shirley privately, not anxious for it but aware that a woman and two children might make Jason think twice about bringing Leah home for seduction while Cora was at work.

Kenya sat on the couch in Shirley's office, a thin, angular girl with Oriental features and African-black skin, huddled next to the armrest as if it would protect her, eyeing Cora's seasonal green suit with open distrust. Unnecessarily, she bounced her sleeping baby on her shoulder. Her little girl, confused, pulled ornaments from the Christmas tree.

"How long I got to stay in somebody's house?" she asked Shirley.

"Just till we feel like it's safe for you here," Shirley said. "It'll be all right."

"How do I know he don't get the address and track me there? Her heat filled the room, but the girl was more afraid than angry, and her voice held no conviction.

"He won't follow you, and he wouldn't get in even if he did," Cora said. "We train people to make sure nothing like that happens."

Kenya looked down, unbelieving but submissive. Sometimes the women came in filled with a healthy fury, but often they left their men in a sudden burst of self-preservation, and when the adrenaline wore off and the pain set in, they were more abject than vengeful. Kenya's bruise was barely visible on her dark skin, but her chin was so swollen, so puffed out from the pretty, angular face that the jaw, from this angle, actually looked misshapen.

The baby suddenly squalled. Abstractedly, Kenya leaned over and pulled an empty bottle from a shabby purse on the couch beside her.

"Come in the kitchen, I'll show you the formula and where to warm it," Cora said. The shelter would provide food if necessary, but the women had to prepare it themselves. Make them independent. Heal their wounds and give them strength. Ordinarily Shirley would be the one to introduce Kenya to the kitchen, but Cora judged that if she were taking the girl home, she might as well take charge.

Pale light from a bank of windows fell into the kitchen, onto surfaces of cheerful tile and golden wood. But as Cora retrieved a saucepan from the cabinet and handed it to Kenya, the girl was surveying the room not for coziness but for safety: the double locks on the door, the fence around the parking lot in back (its gate never closed, however, because of fire regulations). When the bottle was ready, Kenya sat on a kitchen chair, her daughter wide-eyed at her feet, clinging to her leg, the baby with his head lolling off the edge of her arm, his neck unsupported. Keep hold of his head, Cora thought but didn't say. Kenya stuck the bottle into the baby's mouth. He slurped, fell into a brief gluttonous sleep, woke with a start and shrieked.

Cora had taken a woman home once before. Jason had sulked, his space invaded. Seth had tried to make conversation. The woman had muttered back in a thick ghetto accent. She'd stayed two nights, but it seemed like weeks.

Burp him now, Cora thought. For a long time the girl didn't. Cora reached out, gave the girl no choice but to let her lift him up and away, his body against her shoulder, his hair a soft black fuzz against her chin. "What's his name?" she asked.

"Robere."

Or it might have been Andre or LaToya or Jacques. Did every woman who ended up at the shelter give her child a French-sounding name? Did it mark them?

Cora had no crib. No formula. No infant seat. She handed the baby back and weighed her reluctance against the girl's wound. If she were Shirley, she wouldn't hesitate. Shirley had taken several of them home until her landlord got wind of it and threatened eviction. If not for that, she'd be doing it still. She made Cora feel diminished for weighing the trouble of tending this frightened, hostile, battered girl against the comfort of having someone in the house to chaperone her libidinous son.

In the end she needn't have worried. Before another hour had passed, a volunteer had not only offered her home, but had driven in and taken Kenya off. Back in her office, tall-windowed and miniblinded, away from the rising pandemonium of waking children and too many women ready to fix supper, Cora finally thought to buzz Shirley's office and say, "I don't think that girl had the faintest idea about taking care of that baby. Even though it was her second."

"Wouldn't be surprised. Her people are all out of state. She's been here three months with nobody."

"What happened, exactly?" Cora asked.

"He got drunk. Beat the shit out of her."

"The usual," Cora said.

⁂

Seth was in ecstasy. Oh, Mr. Ecstasy himself. He'd just won his age group in the holiday road race, a 5K, with a better time than he'd run in a year. His face had remained healthy red, not pale, even as he sprinted the last hundred meters, blasting around a runner half his age, looking like a man in his thirties instead of twenty years older. He was still flushed as he held his trophy after the awards ceremony, standing under one of the leafless willow oaks that lined the road, holding forth to friends from the local running club about the yellow ribbons encircling the trees.

"Coward's color," he said with disgust. "Get the hostages out and then get out yourself. I hope we're beyond that. When you're up against a bully, you don't give yourself excuses. You support your troops and you go in there and get him."

An old story, this. When Jason was small for his age and plagued by larger boys, Seth could hardly bear the idea that his son might be intimidated. For weeks Jason had stalked the yard, shooting imaginary adversaries with a toy pistol, afraid to go to school. "What do you expect to accomplish by this? The gun doesn't even look real," Seth told him. He encouraged Jason to fight back; he began to show him how. When Cora protested that it was wrong to teach violence, better to talk it out, Seth grew furious. "And what's he going to do when the kid's got his fist in his face?" he roared. "Reason with him?"

To Jason he'd said, "Don't worry about getting banged up a little, just be sure you do some damage in return. That way he'll think twice about coming after you again." So Jason faced his nemesis, came home only marginally worse for the wear, and wasn't bothered again. Now Seth apparently felt for Saddam Hussein the same driving hatred, and extended his distaste to the weather-beaten yellow ribbons that had sprung up everywhere. For himself he bought a patriotic red-white-and-blue ribbon and tied it to the antenna of his car for everyone to see.

"If I were running the show, I wouldn't wait for any January fifteenth deadline, either," he intoned to the runners. "As far as I'm concerned, the sooner the better."

Except for Cora and a few other spectators, the crowd was in sleek nylon shorts and cotton tops, heat only now dissipating from them into the cold morning air. Collectively they zipped their sweatshirts against a sudden wintry wind that sent gray clouds scudding across the sky. Jason had run, too, placing third in his age group behind a couple of college boys, but the young people were having a conversation of their own beyond the line of trees.

"We could be in and out of there in a weekend if we put our minds to it," Seth concluded. Several of the runners nodded.

"Despite the predictions of some experts?" asked a fortyish woman named Trish, sarcastic but smiling, tugging at the black tights she wore under her running shorts.

"Despite the predictions of some experts," Seth countered, returning the smile. At the spate of holiday parties they'd attended so far, people had mostly agreed with him, when for twenty years, on the matter of Vietnam, they hadn't. Being on the winning side pleased him, and now he challenged Trish's gaze until she looked away, pushing a strand of dark hair from her forehead, self-conscious.

Jason surprised her, coming up from behind, laying a hand on her shoulder. In the startled second when she first turned, he might have been a stranger, no longer the target of bullies but larger than the two friends who stood beside him, the bulk of his chest and arms sitting handsomely over his slender frame. His running coach had advised him to take up weight training a year ago, but only recently had the results really begun to show.

"We're going to take off, okay?" Jason said.

"Sure, go on. We'll probably be taking off soon ourselves." Cora looked toward Seth, but he was still holding forth, directing his comments not toward the other men but to Trish. Cora had met the woman before but not noticed her until now, handsome even with her makeup sweated off, high wide cheekbones, a full lush mouth a bit like Cora's.

It occurred to her that when Seth stared at other women, they were often Cora's lookalikes, and she didn't know whether to be upset or flattered. The twinge that went through her felt less like jealousy than embarrassment that Jason was witnessing his father's flirtation. Five years ago—even one year ago—she would have been seized by possessiveness. But now, even when Jason turned hurriedly away with his friends, and when Seth and Trish started laughing together over someone's wry comment, Cora could not have said she was exactly devastated.

She planted Rose Kincaid's Christmas tree in full daylight, in view of anyone who might have seen her go in or out of the yard; it was not meant to be a secret. Rose's brother-in-law had collapsed with a stroke the week after Thanksgiving and died Christmas day. Rose and Joe were staying in New England until they felt the sister-in-law could manage. Their balled-and-burlapped Christmas tree, bought prior to the emergency, had never even been taken into the house. It sat propped against the front porch, protected by overhanging trees but drying out.

To Cora, who'd meant only to go out for a walk, it looked hapless. The air was dry and cold and restless, alternately sunny and cloudy, windy and calm, reflecting her mood. Rose was a friend; she might plant the tree and call the act a Christmas gift; she would tell Rose later. The toolshed in the Kincaid's yard had never locked properly. Cora retrieved a spade, dug a hole in an appropriate spot, piled the loosened fill dirt onto a canvas, added leaf mold from Rose's compost heap. By the time she dragged the tree around back and popped it into the hole, her hair was matted to her head and beads of perspiration trickled down her chest. She hooked up the hose and watered, heart thumping against her ribs as fast as Seth's must have when he was winning his race.

She wasn't at all prepared for the article that appeared in the local section of the newspaper a few days later. "Phantom Gardener Strikes Again." The Rutherfords were quoted on the matter of their pine straw, and Joe Kincaid, who'd left Rose up north yet a while, reported that he'd returned to find a tree planted in his back yard that hadn't been there before.

"The phantom's not malicious, otherwise he wouldn't go around doing people's little garden chores," Peggy Rutherford was quoted as saying. "But still it's frightening, thinking he can come and go like that without being seen."

He.

Cora's throat filled with what she couldn't quite identify as embarrassment or amusement or—oddly—a sense of misplaced power. She'd intended to tell Rose, of course. Now she never could.

"The worst thing he ever did to me wasn't physical, it was what he said," Shirley told the women sitting around the shelter's kitchen table. St. Andrew's Church had sent leftovers from a potluck supper, and Shirley and Cora were having lunch with two residents, Lace McLamb and Kenya Washington, who'd returned from the safe house with her babies. Kenya's bruises were healed, and her hair, newly washed, was pulled back to accentuate her Oriental features, exotic and impossibly youthful.

"See, before I left him, I worked in a job center—it was social work, really," Shirley said, jabbing the air with her fork so that dressing dripped from her speared pasta shells. "You weren't supposed to be supervisor without a degree, but I was the interim one for a long time. Then finally they offered it to me—the first time they ever gave it to somebody who didn't go to college."

Shirley popped the shells into her mouth and chewed while the others took this in. "Well, I was so excited, I could hardly wait for him to get in the door to tell him. He was a truck driver and he was gone a lot. You know what he said to me? He said they probably only asked you because they couldn't get nobody else."

Lace McLamb nodded. Shirley forked up more pasta and looked at Kenya. "I'll tell you. Even now the worst thing I remember about him, it's how bad that hurt. How he made me think there wasn't nothing good enough about me anybody could have wanted."

Kenya stared pointedly down at the table, perhaps embarrassed to be feeling equally unworthy. To the board of directors Shirley often said, "The reason so many of them go back is because even though he beats her, he makes her feel like she doesn't deserve any better. What we try to do is make her feel like she deserves." Kenya lifted her plate and, with exaggerated slowness, moved toward the sink. After the initial fear, there was often this sleepwalking quality to the women, this eerie calm as if they were walking on cotton or floating. From shock? Numbness? Surprise that they'd managed to leave?

Or maybe from the simple quiet that prevailed sometimes, as it did now. After the Christmas rush, the shelter was unusually peaceful, either from the normal post-holiday lull or because the community was collectively poised for a more distant, less personal, war. There'd been no recent late-night calls to the crisis line, no broken bones, no belligerent men. Some shelters wouldn't take women like Kenya back after a man had pursued them there, but Shirley had convinced the board that theirs should. "If you don't, then you're holding her accountable for what he does to her. That's one more reason it's hard for her to leave." The shelter's experience had been that most of the men didn't think to come back to the center itself once the women had been sent away, even for overnight. They assumed the women were gone for good. Since Kenya's return, Shirley had gotten her enrolled in a child care course to help her tend her baby, sent her to social services for food stamps and public housing applications, had a volunteer drive mother and babies to the health department.

Still with that sleepwalker's quality, Kenya turned on the tap and started to rinse her plate. Her children had both fallen asleep down the hall in the playroom, from which the beep-beep of children's TV programming could be dimly heard.

"Sometimes you wish you could do him like he done you," Lace McLamb said, a big woman who looked like she very well could have. "Just once."

Shirley shook her head a vigorous no, though Cora knew that once, when Shirley's husband came in bragging about his other women, Shirley had chased him out with the knife she'd been using to cut onions, and actually shattered his windshield with the blade.

"He's always going to be stronger than you, some ways," Shirley said to Lace. "You can't use his weapons. You have to fight him with your own."

In Jason's open desk drawer, Cora found a body building magazine, three unfiltered Camels and a package of condoms. Even without that, she would have known what had happened. He'd been victorious, which meant, in some way, that Leah had not.

"I might go study at Brian's," he said when she came downstairs, making no move to get up. "If she calls here, let her leave a message."

"I thought you always wanted me to give her Brian's number."

"Naah. Just tell her I'm out."

Cora was reminded of a time when he was twelve or thirteen, still small for his age, running those early races when he was consistently outpaced by another boy. "If I don't beat Todd I'm going to kill myself!" he'd yelled in frustration one day. Cora had been enraged. "I don't ever want to hear you talk like that! About killing yourself over a race! Don't ever let me hear that kind of talk again. It's just a sport."

What she remembered was this: that Seth had scoffed at her agitation. "In a way," he'd said, "everything's a sport."

In those terms, how did one define Leah? Teammate? Opponent? Or the equivalent of the badminton birdie? The soccer ball?

A song played on Jason's tape deck, not his usual rock but loud, raucous country. A taunt. "Hey there, Saddam..." The words followed her into the laundry room. "...not really afraid...of your starving armies and all your wore-out tanks." She couldn't make it all out. Then he must have turned it up. "Don't give us a reason..."

"For heaven's sake, Jason!"

"To come gunning for you!" the singer rasped.

"Turn that down!"

More instructions to Saddam. "Take your poisoned gas and stick it up your....

"Jason!"

"...sassafras."

She came out of the laundry room, into the den. "I mean it Jason. Turn it down. Don't give me a reason."

The volunteer who brought laundry detergent to the shelter once a month as a donation had switched to the new space-saving containers of extra-strength powder.

"How could you go through a whole box of this in a day and a half?" Cora asked Kenya Washington on a day when Shirley was at the dentist and a volunteer was watching the phones. "There're only six people living here right now, and I know half of them didn't do laundry yesterday. This stuff is supposed to do forty-two loads."

"How it gonna do forty-two loads, a box this size?" Kenya asked.

"It's that new kind of detergent. You're only supposed to put in this one little scoop." Cora lifted the small scoop that came in the box to show her.

"I don't care what they say, that ain't gonna do no forty-two loads of dirty laundry," Kenya said. "Not baby laundry with spit-up and all."

Kenya put her hands to her slim hips and stood firm with conviction. Cora almost smiled at the gesture. She made a mental note to tell the volunteer to go back to the old kind of detergent.

The war was on! Desert Shield had become Desert Storm. Finally. During prime time, too! They sat together in the family room, Seth wielding the remote like a weapon, NBC to CBS to ABC and finally to CNN where reporting was better. They had the air strikes with dessert and coffee. The maps of the Persian Gulf. Commentary from Atlanta. Strategy from the Pentagon. On-site reporting from the Al Rasheed Hotel in downtown Baghdad. The heart of enemy territory. Imagine! Tracer bullets. Anti-aircraft bursts. Explosions lighting up the darkness like the Fourth of July. They used that term repeatedly. Fourth of July.

"You think incoming and outgoing sound the same until the first time you actually feel incoming," Seth said, switching channels again, color high. Jason's face echoed his father's.

The next night, as cozy as the first, made Cora think they hadn't had such togetherness in years.

The reporter in Jerusalem was frightened. He'd come into the bureau when the air raid sirens sounded, and had been reporting for some time, wearing his gas mask, wandering around the office while a cameraman filmed messy desks and a dark sky out the window. Other reporters arrived, anonymous in their gas masks.

But wait. It was Tel Aviv that was getting the brunt of the SCUD missiles, not Jerusalem at all. An all-clear was sounded. The reporter took his gas mask off. Was it hours of airlessness that hit him? His sleepless night? His face went pale, he kept running his hands nervously through his hair, he looked like he was going to pass out.

Another newscaster, a woman now. She was taking over, talking so her nervous colleague could compose himself. Switching to Tel Aviv for an update by phone.

"Let me ask him something before you sign off," the pale man said. Shuffling his feet, fingering his hair.

"Calm down, buddy," Jason told the TV, popping open a Coke.

"He's lost it," Seth added.

"I feel sorry for him," Cora said. "He spent half the night in a gas mask. He hasn't had any sleep."

"That's what he's getting paid for."

"Larry has a question for you," the woman said to the man in Tel Aviv.

"See, maybe he's getting it together."

But first, a break to the States.

Some strategic question, perhaps? A political matter? Cut to the Pentagon. To Atlanta. Back to Jerusalem at last. To the crucial question.

"What did you want to ask him?" the woman said. "Uh—Richard. How are you all doing there in Tel Aviv?"

"That was the question?" Seth asked.

"I don't think this speaks well for his career," Jason said.

"I think he's on the next plane out of there," Seth added.

"You have to feel sorry for him," Cora told them.

"For screwing up?" said Seth. "Why?"

Cora and Shirley had driven an hour in the dark, coming back from a workshop on shelter management. They'd left Shirley's car in the shelter parking lot so Cora could drive; it made no sense for both of them to. When they pulled into the lot it was nearly midnight, cold and so clear that the stars were like hard specks of brightness on an inverted black bowl.

"You should have seen her," Cora said. "So incensed that I'd question how much soap they were using. Hands on her hips..."

They both laughed. They were tired and not wary, talking about Kenya Washington. Shirley opened the door.

A figure moved out of the shadows so swift and silent that before they had time to register danger, he'd grabbed Shirley's arm, wrenched it behind her, and pressed a gun hard to the side of her neck. Shirley's coat gaped open, making the fabric of her blouse press tight against her overlarge breasts. Cora's first stupid emotion was embarrassment, at seeing her friend so ungainly and exposed.

"You get out, too, or she gets it," the man told Cora. Fear hit her then, sharp in her nostrils like the scent of something burning. In the space of a second she considered leaning on the horn, stepping on the gas, shifting to reverse and charging backwards toward the street. Finally, obedient, she cut the ignition and let herself out into a frigid slice of air.

The man, she saw, was Howard Washington.

"Now we're gonna go inside, and I'm gonna talk to my wife," he said, low. Pushing Shirley toward the shelter's back door as he spoke, twisting Shirley's arm until her face grew taut and expressionless, concentrating on not showing the pain.

"Get the key," he said to Cora.

She did. Her fingers were shaking; her mind went flat. They stood close in the doorway, the mellow waxy odor of Howard Washington heating the air, a combination of greasy hair dressing and sweat and anger. But no liquor, no glassy cocaine-high. Just a nervous, calculated sobriety.

The back door led into the kitchen, a sudden whoosh of heat.

A night light glowed over the sink and into the empty silence of a sleeping house. Howard pulled Shirley in a little tighter. "I know you got Kenya here," he said, caressing the pistol with his thumb. "Now we're all going to upstairs and get her." He nodded his head toward Cora. "You show us the way and your friend walks right here with me."

The refrigerator motor switched on with a hum as he propelled them into the hall. No question of getting to a phone. The panic button was twenty feet in front of them, on the front wall, but hardly inconspicuous. Shirley said nothing, locked in stillness and subservience. Howard Washington pressed his thin frame against her, not half as wide as Shirley's. He played the pistol up and down her neck.

What was wrong with this picture?

"We'll just bring her down here, and nobody has to get hurt," he said. A trio in slow motion now, inching down the hall toward the stairway. Did she hear movement upstairs? Maybe not.

Ten feet from the alarm. Five. She'd have to lift her hand to press it. Not possible.

If they don't shoot at once, Seth always said, they probably aren't going to shoot at all. She slowed down.

"Keep your ass moving lady, or your friend here gets it."

"We better, Cora," Shirley whispered urgently. Her blouse was bright, electric orange, a power color. A Christmas gift from her children.

Howard Washington, Cora saw, was hardly older than Jason. "You expect us to go up there and get her with you pointing that gun? Is that how you want her to see you?" she asked. Buying a few seconds to study him. If the blood would stop rushing through her ears, she could think.

"I ain't gonna tell you twice," he said, reeling Shirley in. Shirley's eyes were black marbles, circles of fear.

Cora moved down the hallway, toward the stairs. She thought she saw a woman appear at the top, then shy away. He was at the wrong angle to see her.

What he saw was the red knob protruding from the wall, the panic button.

"Move away from that thing, bitch." He pointed the gun at Cora.

You can't use his weapons to fight him.

She moved away. Up the stairs. Slowly. Slowly.

"Freeze!"

He turned, startled, clutching Shirley tight. Two policemen were poised at the bottom of the stairs, weapons drawn. The women upstairs must have called them. Howard Washington was the only one surprised to see them.

"You come any closer and I'll blow her away," he said. Shirley wore no expression at all; she might have been standing at attention. Or absent. Or at the end-point of terror, to have escaped a brutal husband, to have come this far, to meet her end at the hands of a teenager. Cora thought then she finally understood the meaning of the term, beaten.

She remembered Kenya, with her hands on her hips, sure of something.

Howard pulled Shirley into him, holding the gun pointed toward her head, a few inches away from it to be sure everyone could see.

That's when Cora knew all she needed to about weapons. "It's a toy," she whispered. And then louder to the men at the bottom of the stairs. "The gun's a toy."

The police moved then. It took Shirley a second to register freedom, but when she did she moved away with more grace than you'd credit in a woman her size, and in thirty seconds it was over.

They couldn't sleep, not after all that. Cora didn't get home until two-thirty, having called Seth earlier to give him a brief outline. To her surprise, he arrived at the shelter while the police were still taking their report. Cora stood with Seth's hand on her shoulder, watching Kenya and Shirley give their statements, each dazed and almost cushioned—Shirley by her size and sturdiness, Kenya by her gaunt beauty—and yet, in contrast to Cora's coupled state, entirely alone. When Seth followed her home in his car, unasked, the gesture seemed wholly an act of love. Later they lay in bed stretched out flat in the darkness, hands behind their heads, rehashing the evening.

"How did you know the gun wasn't real?" Seth asked.

"I told you—Jason."

"I don't know how you could be so sure." He looked up at the dark ceiling, unmoving.

"Remember how Jason used to have all those guns when he was little? When the bullies were after him? And how you used to say they didn't look like the real thing?"

"Nowadays they do," he said. "People rob stores with toy guns. They rob banks. The weapons look completely authentic."

"This one didn't."

"You could have been wrong." He sat up and turned on the bedside lamp so as to impress her with the force of his gaze.

A tremor went through her, then melted away. It was too late to be frightened. She smoothed the crease of worry that formed between his brows. "No," she said. "I knew."

Still bathed in his concern, she turned out the light and slid closer, running her hand along his mottled skin and touching the paunches at his sides. This made her try to pull her own stomach in—not with much success—and unaccountably, she wanted to laugh. What was squeezing her stomach so ineffectively was not muscle mass but old age, she supposed—hers, and his, too. Then Seth pulled her toward him with such urgency that it seemed not to matter. In spite of temptations like Trish, he was not likely to leave her, or she him. They would probably spend their next twenty years together exploring their mutual and advancing flab.

She forgot herself then—because what worse could she think of than mutual and advancing flab?—and the touching was better. As if, in some way, even though one system was shutting down, another was taking over.

Jason sat on the deck in shorts and t-shirt, attached by earphones to his radio, goose bumps dotting his bulging arms against one of those warm spells that briefly graced the southern winter. Today wasn't as warm as it looked. A few feet from him in the yard, admiring her bounteous blooming camellias, Cora hugged herself into her windbreaker.

"You ought to put some clothes on," she called, forcing Jason to lift his headphone away from his ear to hear her.

"I'm all right. I need some color."

"What? A red nose from the cold you'll get?"

"A gorgeous February tan." He extended an arm, flexed the biceps, studied it lovingly. She was already annoyed with him for his recent swaggering attitude, and this gesture didn't endear him to her.

The condoms in his drawer had been supplemented by others in his wallet and (until Seth spoke to him about it) the glove compartment of the car. At the same time, he'd started going to parties with other boys instead of Leah, and to brag about flirting with Leah's friends. In Cora's view, Leah was being nicer than he deserved. Her notes had taken on a sort of pathetic dignity.

I've given you something I can never give anyone else. I'm not sorry. I've learned more from you than I have from anyone. I've learned how to study and apply myself. But I'll tell you this honestly: I don't want to lose you.

Still preening, Jason looked down to see if his chest muscles were visible through his too-tight shirt. They were, but only because he'd taken to wearing shirts a size or two smaller than before. Cora pointed toward the yard next door, where the four-year-old played in the sandbox. He was a tiny boy, even smaller for his age than Jason had once been.

"If you ask nicely," she said, "maybe you can borrow some shirts from him."

"Very funny, Mom." Jason snapped the earphones back to his head and closed his eyes against Cora's sourness. The more he fell in love with himself, the more he felt entitled to ignore her. She extracted the pruning shears she'd been carrying in her pocket, turned away from the camellias, and began cutting what might have been deadwood (but was impossible to tell now, in the dormant season) from her rosebushes.

Head back, eyes closed, the wispy beginnings of whiskers dotting his upraised chin, Jason offered his face to the light. Seth opened the screen and soft-shoed around him. "He's sunning the body beautiful, I see," he said to Cora.

"Working on a case of pneumonia," she replied. Jason's radio was so loud that they could hear a faint beep of it wafting out from the earphones. He might have been on another planet.

Seth lugged a chair off the deck and sat near Cora in the yard. She dropped down beside him, watching him pluck a few strands of bristly grass. "I did a damned fool thing the other day," he said.

"What?"

"I went to Army headquarters to see if they needed any middle-aged ex-officers to help out while they've got so many guys in the Gulf."

"I didn't know you were interested in doing that."

"Neither did I."

Embarrassed, they both stared ahead of them, at sun on the brown grass, at the bright green camellia leaves, the show of pink and white blossoms.

"The upshot is, they don't really need you if you've been out twenty years," he said.

She didn't know how to reply. It seemed an enormous confession.

"You've got your business, anyway," she managed finally. "You couldn't really leave."

He shrugged and flicked the strands of grass away from him.

"What really makes you feel like a jerk, though, is doing something to try to relive your youth. When you know damn well that's impossible."

A garden center had sent a box of unsold flower bulbs to the shelter, nearly a hundred altogether. The bare sunny spot behind the shelter cried out for beautification, but it was late in the season for planting bulbs, and every time they lined up a volunteer, it either got cold or rained. The box sat in the corner of Shirley's office, untouched and accusatory, until she said one day, "What we need is that phantom gardener," and sent a pure jolt of adrenaline through Cora's veins.

They were sitting on the floor at the time, paperwork for the new budget spread out all around them, Cora juggling figures on a hand calculator. She felt her face go red as if from a hot flash, but Shirley didn't notice.

"We got all this mess to bother with," Shirley said, indicating the papers. "So you'd think some guy that likes to garden so much would come down here and help us out."

"Maybe he's out of business," Cora finally managed. "I don't think he's done anything lately."

Her back ached from sitting on the floor among the papers. Her head, too. Funding from two different grants was being cut.

They'd spent the whole day trying to pare the budget.

"What I don't understand is why he picks a neighborhood like yours instead of coming down here where we need it," Shirley said, joking.

Cora set down the calculator and tried to straighten her back. The heat in her face really was a hot flash. She stood and fanned herself, coming face to face with her reflection in the mirror over the couch.

Beads of sweat had formed above her upper lip, but her cheeks were not flushed, her ears not red, none of the great visible upheaval she had expected. She said to Shirley lightly, "Maybe he's racist. Maybe he just doesn't like women."

Sortie. She hadn't even known the word two months ago. Now it was fixed permanently in her mind. Sorties in the air and operations on the ground. Death by friendly fire. Iraqis surrendering by the dozen. Seth claimed he'd grown tired of CNN's coverage, but after supper when he started watching a sitcom on another channel, he lasted perhaps five minutes before he switched back.

Cora heard the news dimly in the distance as she pulled laundry out of the dryer. In the kitchen, Jason talked on the phone in low and serious tones. When he was finished he trailed Cora to the washing machine. "I broke it off," he said.

"With Leah, you mean?"

"It's better, isn't it? I never really liked her that much. I mean, it wasn't really fair."

Cora did not say, you mean not fair to screw her and not care about her? She folded a towel.

"Also, she was getting so attached. Scott Newman wanted to date her. You know Scott. But he couldn't, with me around."

"Scott Newman likes her?"

"When I told her I wanted to break it off, she asked me if I meant we should only go out sometimes," Jason said. "But I said I thought we shouldn't go out at all. That's better, isn't it? A clean break?" He looked earnestly troubled. He leaned against the door jamb. He looked younger than he had.

"I always thought a clean break was easier in the long run," she said. His distress charged the heated the room. She knew the helplessness of not being able to love someone back. The fierceness of repulsion. She hadn't married till thirty, after all. She'd once left a date in the middle of a restaurant because she couldn't bear to be with him a moment longer.

Had she really done such a thing? Yes.

But still she didn't forgive Jason.

I never thought I'd have a child, she wanted to say. She picked up a pile of towels and headed for the linen closet. I was thirty-five. Old, in those days, to be a first-time mother.

He followed her.

I thought you were entirely precious, she thought. "When you get older," she told him, "you'll learn the value of kindness."

Out in her garden, by the slant of light that drifted from the den, she cut camellias from each bush—not so many that the loss would show—and filled the empty laundry basket.

There was no longer such a thing as bomber's moon, the reporters said. Moonlight made the planes visible to anti-aircraft gunners. No, a pitch-black night was better for sorties these days, when infrared and laser-guided bombs could hit targets through inky darkness.

There was no moon as she drove to Leah's house with the laundry basket in her trunk. No light at all after she cut her headlights. The blossoms, as she scattered them across the yard, spelled out, she hoped, the name of Leah's admirer, Scott.

In time, she would tell Shirley. On a day when things had been dismal, when women like Kenya Washington went back to the men who'd beaten them, when Shirley was repeating statistics in consternation: "It makes no sense that she has to leave five to seven times before she stays away."She would keep the secret till then. I'm the phantom gardener, she would say.

Oh, right, Shirley would reply.

I am.

Cora, you're a crazy woman.

Yes, probably.

They would laugh.

She came back to Seth at the TV and Jason on the phone again, telling a friend about the breakup. Bragging? In the den, the screen showed clips of beige tanks on beige desert, the desolation of sand.

"Cold out there?" Seth asked.

"Not if you move around."

Jason hung up. Restless, he bounded up the stairs. And down again. Refrigerator opening. Closing. Up the steps.

"I look at him and you know what I don't see?" she asked Seth.

"What?"

"I don't see the skinny six-year-old who got beat up on the bus. I don't see the kid who couldn't quite win a race and wanted to so much. What I see now is a kid who has sex with girls and then dumps them."

He put his hand over hers. "I think he was just scared. He won't be that way forever. He'll be all right." In the dim light his skin was still smooth, a little puffy around the wedding ring but not yet marred with veins.

Jason filled the doorway, can of Pepsi in one hand, bag of chips in the other. He came in, plunked down in front of the newscast without a word. Apparently he had no one left to call, nothing left to do. Cora was sticky under her shirt, hot from strewing blossoms. Cut to the Pentagon. The White House. Seth and Jason focused on the screen, so intent and passive that the sight of them made her sad. "I'm going to take a shower," she said finally, loving them perhaps more than she had but grateful, too, that for the moment, at least, she was not reduced to watching the war on television.

Lisa Martinović

AND JOHN WAYNE, HE STANDS UP FOR HIS BELIEFS

you're having a discussion with this man
concerning the tiresome, media-flagellated story
about which public opinion has settled uneasily into distinct camps
either
the vicious scum bucket of a wife beater really did the dirty deed and
is now reaping the benefits of a right-fucking-on jury nullified verdict
or
the white racist LAPD framed yet another innocent black man and
has at last been exposed down to the skid marks in its collective shorts
yes
this much is obvious
yet the man seated comfortably before you opines with some vigor that
OJ should get the Congressional Medal of Honor
for cuttin' the cum-sucking throat of that bitch what done him so wrong

what do you do with such a man
a man so far off the map of civilized discourse that
your circuits snap crackle and pop
in the futile attempt to comprehend his madness

do you
calmly try to explain what look to you like flaws in his logic
run screaming for the nearest women's separatist commune
say 20 Hail Mary's and pray for divine intervention
or do you kneel down gently
place your lips around his cock
and go ahead and do what you always do
because this man
this man who had this thought
who said this thing
yes, *this man*
is your man

then what do you tell a man whose first response
to the Oklahoma City bombing is:
they oughta start shootin' ragheads on sight
Do you remind him that your best friend is Lebanese and

does he want to off her, too
or do you wait *one day* and gloat in sweet silence when
the culprits are revealed to be US Army issue good ole white boys
weaned on Wonder Bread, Budweiser and a vengeful God

and what to make of a man who has
for two years resisted
your every well-intentioned and misguided attempt to
facilitate his transformation from Stone Age to New Age
this man you've spent lifetimes of energy on
feverishly urging him like a recalcitrant sunflower
to grow towards the light
that's right I mean do some psycho-spiritual growth work
read this book, listen to that tape, do these exercises
and for god's sake get on the fucking path to spiritual enlightenment

and just when you think all your glorious wisdom has fallen
on prejudice-encrusted ears
one day he sits up and sez
baby, I want to see some changes too
and you get all excited like maybe he's finally seen a candle if not
the whole damn burning bush
and you pant: Tell me!
and he sez
I want you to start wearing a bra when we go to town so
other men can't see your nipples

and you begin to know
what to do
what you must do
with such a man

you sit him down and through the tears you say
I love the man I imagine lies within you
I can't even live with the man you are

Farewell, you sigh
peeling off your panties:
how do you want it tonight?

Elizabeth Oakley

BLOOD ROOT

Blood blossoms burst forth in Ireland,
Iraq, while the roots stretch deep.
I feel them when we fight and I want
to burn your tongue black with hot rock
rather than listen to words opposing
mine; engorged roots strike through limbs—
my hand, your face.

Robin Jacobson

BLOOD

everywhere, you don't have to look
as far away as Sarajevo or Beijing. Right next door,
there's blood in your neighbor's eyes—
remember how sour he was when Desert Storm was over
so fast. Closer, inside your own heart.
You don't know how to get what you want
without drawing blood. Usually your own.
And always you leave stains, scars—evidence
of longing. C'mon, admit it.
You're hungry. Don't give a damn
about poetry or cult flicks anymore,
tired of listening to someone else try to explain
desire or make it look like art,
you want to leave your seat at the Paradise,
hike up your dress in the alley and
ride between your ex-lover and the cold brick
just before the late show
lets out. But you're so used to being good,
you stay in your seat, watch him
cross his legs in the blue
flicker, watch his sandaled foot dangle
like a white stallion dipping its head down to drink,
when all you want to do is go back
to his place, pull him down
on the deep-pile wall-to-wall and ride him,
run his lips between your teeth like mangoes,
swallow him the way swallows swallow mosquitoes
on a lake at dusk—wait!—
that's too clean and quiet and you want it
feral, the way that raccoon took the stray cat
under your window last night, both screeching.
You'd leave his bones behind as a warning,
splintered, traces of marrow caked at the corners
of your mouth. And prints, whorls of fingertips
oily on the doorknob, red lips on a nail
still burning in an ashtray when the cops come.

Hannah Wilson

CERTAIN SLANTS OF LIGHT

i

What is the legend—whoever
looks full into the light of truth
goes blind? The way a vagrant
walking down railroad tracks
might round a curve,
see the Cyclopean eye,
wave his arms like a Christ un-nailed
not realize he has time
to jump.

ii

When it got too dark on the bus
to read, the woman I sat next to
told me it took her five years to say
he was a mean-spirited, good-for-
nothing son-of-a-bitch. Now
when friends talk
of her sainted husband
she says it over to herself
like a mantra: he was
a mean-spirited, good-for—

iii

We angle back into the lives
of our dead. My Uncle Ben
walked into the Atlantic
in a brown gabardine suit and leather shoes.
Older now than he was then, able
to give name to his illness and
money to its sufferers,
I remember only his slumped figure
standing in the corner of a dark porch,
his graveled complaint:
Don't play ball on the stoop.

iv

A friend gave me this image as a gift,
a line of light under her door.
When she heard his footsteps in the hall
she lay still, prayed
he would keep going—to the bathroom,
back again to her mother's bed, down
to the kitchen, anywhere
but where his feet blocked her light.

Earth between them now, he sleeps
in dark safety. But sometimes she gets up
and walks that old hallway,
stands outside her old room,
blocks the light she cannot
turn off at the switch.

v

We want grace to let light play full
upon ourselves. We lie
still unable to turn the knob
from inside, or unwilling
to expose to white nothingness
what stands there waiting.

PART TWO
WAR ZONE
THE DAMAGE WE DO TO ONE ANOTHER

Tragedy is. . . a representation of an action that is worth serious attention, complete in itself and of some amplitude . . . by means of pity and fear bringing about the purgation of such emotions.

—Aristotle
Poetics

Everyone has the right to tell the truth about her own life.

—Ellen Bass and Laura Davis
The Courage to Heal

If you come as softly
as wind within the trees
you may hear what I hear,
see what sorrow sees.

—Audre Lorde
"Memorial I"

editor's note

The works in this section reveal the range of things that go wrong in adult relationships: partner abuse, harassment, exploitive sex, rape, verbal assaults, deepening rifts, even murder. Many of these writings are first-hand accounts of lived experience. Others are creative reenactments which attempt to understand abusive experiences from the inside. Both of these strategies offer important insights into the dynamics of relational inequities and their consequences. The voices, styles and perspectives these writers use, like the kinds of abuse they describe, are varied and complex.

In the pages that follow, for example, you will read "Lifelines," Nancy Casey's heroic and moving account of an abusive relationship and her escape. Jennifer Stone's "Male Strom" and M. Tarn Wilson's "To My Mother and Sister about that Thing that Happened in Denver" both recreate the trauma of rape. In a piece that walks the line between fiction and fact, Alice Crane writes about the impact of alcohol on intimacy, while Paul Truttman, now in San Quentin, shares his story about spousal abuse that ended in murder. Some authors write in the voice of a fictional persona using their imaginations to step inside the mind of an abuse survivor as Kim Addonizio does in her story, "Inside Out," and Laura Goodman in "The Sound of Speed." These recreations are especially moving because of the ways they incarnate the emotional trauma that results from abuse.

While it has not been as widely documented or sensationalized as heterosexual abuse, intimate violence is also an issue in the gay community, as poems by Thomas Avena and Jeff Walt, and fiction by Martha Clark Cummings and Melissa Capers attest. Whatever the gender relationships concerned, violence seems to arise from similar sources: power imbalances of various kinds, social pressures from outside the relationship, inequities because of money or class, substance abuse, or old wounds, all fed by elements within our culture that condone and even laud violence as an emblem of power.

Throughout the diverse writings that follow, we are unflinchingly shown the complexity of intimate violence. But these authors do not simply recount atrocities. They also offer insight, courage, wisdom, humor, sensitivity and creative brilliance. At times, the passion of their revelations is deeply cathartic; at other times, their candor is unnerving. Above all, they convey a vitality and intensity that will stay with you long after you have finished reading them. As Muriel Rukeyser has written, "In time of crisis, we summon up our strength. Then, if we are lucky, we are able to call every resource, every forgotten image that can leap to our quickening, every memory that can make us know our power." This describes what these writers have achieved. **—E. C.**

Alice Crane

HOT RED PEPPER

I often fell for my teachers, and sometimes I fell hard enough to let them know I was available. But not this one. He's the one who came on to me, on a field trip to Chicago for a class in American Indian Politics. That was before Native American became the p.c. term.

He kissed me hard as we emerged onto the street from eating breakfast at a Mexican restaurant. Hot red pepper at nine in the morning. I'd never been kissed with such intensity. It was the weekend I was told Indians are the best bridge builders in the world, the only ones who can work fearlessly on narrow steel girders so high above the teeming river.

My teacher Jake was one hundred percent Indian, reservation born and raised, and now a graduate student in political science. He was married to a white woman—his second marriage, her first. Thirteen years older than me, overweight, alcoholic, already drunk at nine in the morning. His eyes rolled dangerously when he kissed me on the streets of Chicago, and mine careened wildly as I kissed back.

He took me to his hotel room, at nine in the morning, fucked me like I was a whore. Entered me from the back, from the side, legs lifted, legs bent, finally on top of me came, hours later, so drunk he almost didn't remember who I was.

Turned me on to sweet bread and hot red chili, turned me on to screwdrivers for breakfast, turned me on—this fat, married Indian.

Jake knocked at my apartment door at 3:40 every morning for two years—3:30 being the time in our town when all the bars closed—taught me how to fuck dirty, taught me how to fuck. I never came before I fucked that Indian, that medicine man, that Eagle dancer. But always, with him, I came—he fucked so long, so drunk. Always, I had three or four orgasms a night, awake till dawn, fucking. "Oh it feels so good," I would say. "You like my little man?" he would answer. "My cock? My hot red pepper?" And he would hold it out to me in the palm of his hand, offering me his most holy of holies.

Past dawn, his wife would call. "Is he there?" Or later, after the first year of this, she would just say, "Send him home." At least he was with me, not some stranger. Or so I imagined she was thinking.

I became almost her friend, a phone buddy, the other wife. She could count on me not to stir things up, not to ask for more than her man wanted to give, not to offer more than she could take. I was second wife, an after-the-bars-close fuck, reliable. She could sleep, raise the kid, work her full-time job while the husband finished his Ph.D., all because I was there for him, his sweet fuck, there for him so that she didn't have to be there in that way.

He wore me out some nights. A full-time student, I was working on two degrees, working also half-time as a library clerk to pay my rent, buy my food. On weekends, I canoed wild rivers, wrote letters to Congressmen, ordered them to stop the Army Corps of Engineers from building more dams.

Twenty years old, I might have had a daytime lover, someone sober, someone who didn't sob on my shoulder, rant about the evils of white people. I was white and guilty as hell, this in the year *Bury My Heart at Wounded Knee* was published. Everyone figured I was working through some karmic bond, or even working out karma for the whole white race. Sure, but this Indian could fuck, too. And he was man, not boy. And oh, the rides he took me on through deep wide rivers of insanity, across high bridges, far into his otherworld mind, his tribal past, his knowledge of medicine ways.

Sometimes I would go with him to bars, or he would visit me drunk, in the daytime, and we would sit outside on the stone wall or stroll through campus hand-in-hand. People shook their heads at us.

You would think I might have felt some embarrassment, some sense of guilt over being with a married man, and I did. But it was slight, because I loved him, really loved him, and I was adept at compartmentalizing, justifying, believing that it all made sense. I rarely thought I might be hurting his wife, believed instead I was helping keep things stable. I was a dependable lover, where otherwise he might have been with a new woman every night. I was there for him, as a friend, and her friend, too, though she glared at me during our occasional encounters. Witless, I smiled at her lovingly as if I were doing no wrong.

Finally, she phoned me before midnight, one full moon night in late November, and said: "How can Jake and I work through our problems together when he can flee to you whenever he wants?"

I heard the sense in that. It happened just as I fell in love with someone else, someone not married, someone not drunk. Then Jake said he had to stop seeing me, his wife had said so. I told him I agreed with her, agreed with them both, it was time to sober up.

But we didn't break off, not right away. First there was a marriage proposal, an exchange of Christmas presents, a lobster dinner, a spat. After that I refused to see him again, period, ever, except in the daytime, for lunch, and only if he was sober. Jake gave up phoning me, but instead kept trying to break down my door at 3:40 every morning for months afterward. When David was there, I asked him to answer the knock. "She doesn't want to see you," he would say. Or, "she's otherwise occupied." Occasionally Jake became belligerent, but more often than not he would meekly withdraw from the door.

When David wasn't there, I sometimes ignored Jake, or spoke through the door in firm tones telling him to go away. I steadfastly refused to open up. Refused to let him into my apartment. My body. My mind.

One early morning in March, near our anniversary, Jake refused to stop pounding on the door. When my apartment-mate became upset by the noise, I let Jake in to shut him up. He was staggering drunk, his eyes rolled back in his head, alcohol reeking from every pore of his body.

"I love you," he sobbed. "I love you. Please get out your guitar, sing me that song!"

Half asleep I played for him and sang, "Oh no, I never got over those blue eyes" (my color), then switched to "brown" (his color). We cried together, both drunk on memory and sentiment and exhaustion.

Just when I rose to escort Jake out the front door, a new energy surged through his body. He jerked the guitar from my hands, dragged me to my bedroom, pushed me down on my mattress. His face blind crazy, he ripped off my underwear, unzipped his pants, and tried to force himself into me, his heavy body shaking with sobs.

I almost let him do it, almost let him enter me again. How different was it really from all those other times? *But it is different,* I told myself. *It is. I don't want him inside of me again. Inside my vagina, inside my head, driving me mad with guilt that has nothing to do with me.*

Summoning all my strength, both physical and mental, I pushed him off me at the last second. He ranted about how I was trying to ruin him, trying to get the goods on him so I could turn him in to the FBI. His words were crazy. Totally crazy. I wondered, *does this prove that I'm crazy, too? Does this prove that I hate myself, carrying on like this for almost two years with a dead-drunk alcoholic who hates white people and treats me like a cunt?*

I thought about calling the police, requesting a restraining order. But Jake left. Subdued, apologetic, he staggered from my apartment that night and continued to leave me alone—until summer, the night of the solstice, the first time I took LSD.

On LSD, all my doors were open, open to the energy of the universe. He knew it, that Indian. He came knocking at my door at the old time, as if nothing were different. "You still love me," he said. "I can feel it."

I could feel it, too, but I refused to make love. Instead, I steered him out to the street, where we walked together until dawn. I sought out my hippie friend Paloma, and like a true friend, she joined us, trying to calm him while he accused me of every evil of which a woman has ever been accused. I didn't try to get away from him. He was making me feel miserable, but I listened. I walked. I companioned him through the streets.

After Paloma left us, Jake and I stopped by a coffee shop for breakfast. He ordered *huevos rancheros*. I tried to be rational, high on LSD, tried to convince him that I was a good white person, while he called me bitch, whore, cunt. Spat in my face. Rubbed hot red pepper on my lips.

I ran from him then. And as I ran my mind leaped toward the memory of my childhood home, meals at the round oak table, my mother's face, twisted by hatred and some unnamed pain as she slapped me in the face at meal time. Again and again and again. Her hand on my face. The heat. The blood rushing from my heart to my face. Again and again. The way I took it. The way I always took it, retreating silently into hurt confusion, wondering what I'd done. When I knew I hadn't done anything. Except be born.

Afterwards, trapped in her arms on my bed, sobbing, I watched her face progress through a range of emotions as she professed her regret and her love. "I didn't mean to hit you, I didn't mean to hit you. I love you. You're Mama's little girl. I would never hurt you. I love you."

Only to be followed again the next day by the open palm. A mocking voice. Ridicule. "You selfish brat. You idiot."

Call that memory a moment of insight, an instant of grace, the connection through image of one hell with another. That connection a link which freed me from further repetition, at least a little. The next time I saw Jake, sober in the daylight with his white wife, I mumbled hello, good-bye and kept on walking. I never saw nor spoke with either of them again.

Only years later would I learn that both my grandfathers were alcoholics. That my father's father committed suicide rather than retreat from his alcoholism. That my mother's father sobered up after ten years of heavy drinking only because my grandmother gave him an ultimatum after he had knocked my adolescent mother down the basement steps as she tried to block his way to a hidden whiskey bottle. My mother has never been able to tell me this directly. I've found out by quizzing relatives and through brief, night-window views into my mother's jumbled inner world.

I have never hated my Indian ex-lover. These days, I remember him more with fondness than distress. I barely recognize the girl who loved him. Still, she lives on in my unhealed heart.

The violent repercussions of my grandfathers' alcoholism still echo through the decades in my mother's mind and mine. We are linked by the red passion. She continues to careen out of control. I stand arrested on the brink. Sometimes, the red is all that is real, everything else a paleness beside it.

Molly Fisk

WALKING DOWN FRANKLIN STREET

It's still there, the weary three-decker.
It still leans inward from the outside walls.
I used to wake up in that house
and lie in bed alone, smiling and looking out
the tall windows at early cars
going by, a neighbor walking his old
slow dog before work. He'd move
out of sight, leave me with sunlight
that spilled in and made a warm
lake of the floor.

Nothing is as simple as it looks.
The man I loved and lived with once threw me
against that front hall wall—stars
floated lightly on the surface
of my eyes, little pieces of white plaster dust
drifted in the air around us. Time went so slow.
I had a chance to think about the precarious
lives of women: anonymous dark Egyptians
hauling water; pioneers in checked sunbonnets
who trudged beside their wagons;
nuns bent over herb gardens in fourteenth-century France.
Waiting for his next move, I saw all the women who were held
against walls, I could hear their thoughts. We were
the same person. Our breasts lifted and fell
in time to each other's ragged breathing, our eyes
slid briefly toward the door before
dragging themselves to his face—the human face
irate: corded neck, eyes raging black, the mouth
contorted into that painful,
unsustainable shape. No one
could hold on to it.

Thomas Avena

WE DESIRE TO BE HERMETICALLY WALLED AWAY FROM VIOLENCE

When very drunk, he struck me,
I answered clearly,

"You don't know me well enough for that."

He was stopped; we took
what remained in the glass . . .

After all the guests had departed,
Piaf on the stereo still sang:
Padam Padam.

We consecrated our dance to inarticulation.

Our incompatibilities animated by drink,
and the vain-glorious theater of the act,
we fought finally and severed . . .

to reunite
between white walls
blank windows,
pride and betrayal carefully, facelessly shelved—

"this apartment conspires against us."

"they reconciled merely to ruin further . . ."

LAND'S END

San Francisco, 1985

During our third or fourth year
of the plague, it was unnaturally warm;

serpentine rocks were laid like cairns,
end to end,
dull green and white.

On slender trails,
ribs carved in the cliff
men passed
in groups of two
or three or alone

first attacked   *the skin*
its bewildering stain—

the body's breach

I wanted to touch each one.

The phrase:

. . .tired of walking
                                        bowed
by fear and uncertainty,

that dim fever

                              ceased . . .

unfettered:
solar
plexus, heart—

a long inhalation
taking in sun, heat, rocky
cliffs, the dazzling sea,

and these late years
of men
passed reflectively
by.

A finger of white
opened a slit
in the blush sky

then, I too followed the men:
Gary, Roland, beautiful
men in unusual ways

*

We step from the burning
sun, where cypress
battered by wind
flatten
against the cliff's recess.

"There are so many ways
other ways
to make love."

"You're exquisite."

"You're drunk."

"It's true!"

*

The sky deepens

I lose the path
and climb,
crushing one pink bloom
single stalk
perfumed, a "naked lady"
to my lips—

a dozen mosquitoes
on my arms, my thighs—

their stings
reprove me: everything
sucks and feeds

still;

graphite clouds
lace
the ultraviolet sky

and leaning
against the stone
portals of Land's End,

his features
washed and blurred
by age, a man
(or the shadow of a man,
the *persona)*

exclaims:

"I want to suck your cock,"

strikes a match—
and his face,
red, elastic
mouth, bruised
eyebrow is

lit.

"At this time of day, your chances,
surely, are diminishing
my dear, dear boy . . ."

Kent Taylor

FOLIE A DEUX

for A.A.R.

We pass madness
back and forth
  like a cold

we're never simultaneously
sane

you assembled yourself
  alias by alias
before stenciling
your secret
  on my shadow

it hides there
like a forgotten double
lost in the silver
of a mirror

I weep at the toilet
dreaming in tongues
catching my tears
in an arc of piss

M. Tarn Wilson

TO MY MOTHER AND SISTER ABOUT THAT THING THAT HAPPENED IN DENVER

In our family, we say "that thing that happened in Denver." We cannot say what that thing is, because the word is as sharp as a knife slicing through a woman's thigh.

He did not hurt us most by breaking open our home and bodies, but by leaving behind a silence, like a mist, through which we cannot hear each other.

This is the story we agree upon: someone, that night, forgot to lock the door. He touched my sister first on her soft spot which had no hair. He did not touch her friend, sleeping on the living room floor beside her. Next, he entered my bedroom. He would have hurt me, we say in our story, because I had new soft hair growing like mouse's fur. But I slipped into the crack between my bed and the wall and slept with the covers pulled over my head. He did not see me, and I did not wake. So, he slid into our mother's room. This is lucky, we say in our story, better that it was our mother, wide already with the birth of two children and familiar with suffering.

We agree upon this, but in our silence, we each have other stories to tell.

In the center of my silence are the locks on the front door, and an overwhelming sense of my own carelessness. I cannot remember, from the two-bedroom house on Emerson, the color of the kitchen counters or whether the front door had small windows or a peep hole, but I can see every detail of the deadbolt: high as my chest, round, an inch thick, copper-colored with dark fingerprints, specks of white paint, a knurled, oval knob. Above the deadbolt, a chain lock, copper and sturdy. Someone, that night, before we went to sleep, forgot to turn the bolt. Someone forgot to slide the chain.

After it is over, I hear our mother say it. Someone forgot to lock the door. Or does she ask it? Who forgot to lock the door? Before they went to sleep, my sister and her best friend in the fifth grade made a nest of blankets on the living room floor. Were they to lock the door after they tired of giggling? But I am the careless one. I daydream while I clean the bathroom, leaving behind triangles of dust and grime which my mother scolds. I am the one who forgets my lunch as I run late to the school bus. So, I am the one who has forgotten to lock the door. I have invited him in.

I was the lucky one, we say in our story, but why should the one who has forgotten have any luck at all? It is a luck I do not want. I usually sleep in the middle of the bed on my stomach, my right cheek on my pillow, my left knee bent. Yet that night, I rolled toward the wall and slipped into the seam between the wall and my bed. Although it was a sticky night, I pulled my blue comforter over my head, suffocating in my own hot breath. My sister watched as he entered my room, our bedroom. I must have known. I must have pulled myself into the dark secrets of my bed and emptied myself so he could not see me. I chose to sleep. I chose to leave them alone.

In our story, we say that it is better that it is our mother, but that statement is a moral to the story which isn't true. For weeks after, when I touched my mother's arm, I could feel her trembling deeply like earthquake aftershocks. We cannot keep our house. She cannot keep her job. The suffering is more than she can bear. He should have found me first and been satisfied. I should have lain open, my mother's lamb. I should have willed myself awake.

I have betrayed them with sleeping, and I have betrayed them with a prayer. Early that same evening, I had been sitting on my mother's unmade bed thinking of God. "I don't know what I think about God," I told her, "but I do think that God is very big and God is Love."

Later, I know that my conclusion about God was a prayer and that prayer protected me. I am angry at this God. A God who is very big, a God who is Love, would love my sister with her skinny legs, her vibrant energy, her blonde hair with tangles like a rat's nest (as our mother says), her urgent insistence upon justice. A God of Love would love my mother who dances to Soul music as she cleans the house, who, when she is almost out of money at the end of the month, splurges on take–out spaghetti from Pizza Heaven, who doesn't mind that Misty, the ill-behaved German shepherd, munches the center of her surprise birthday cake we baked for her and she eats it anyway. Wouldn't a God of Love love even the man who hurt us and heal his animal thoughts and ways? This God of Love should have told me to lock the door.

Or, I have not betrayed them with a prayer but with a wish. That evening, I had been sitting on the floor watching TV, making circles with my fingers in the new beige carpet, looking at the new couch my mother had saved for. I am happy that my mother has a job as a supervisor in an oil company, happy that she bought an expensive pair of culottes from a department store, happy that she isn't on welfare anymore, happy that sometimes a man takes her out on a date. We've lived in the same house for three whole years, and I say to myself, "I hope nothing bad ever happens to us again. We've had our share."

Afterward, I know that I have broken a law. I must never ask to be spared suffering, only for the strength to bear it and the grace to grow from it. When I misplaced my wish, I invited him in to teach me a lesson. I did not even lock the door.

He did not hurt us most by breaking into our home and bodies, but by leaving behind a silence, like a mist, through which we could not hear each other. The thing that happened in Denver. I have named you, thing. You are rape. But beneath the sharpness, like a dagger pulled across a woman's thigh, is the dull thudding pain of another word, guilt. And as I name you, you lift, and beneath you I see another word, forgiveness, and the essence of forgiveness, love.

Jennifer Stone

MALE STROM

Winter 1970
Berkeley, California

And unto them was given power,
As scorpions of the earth have power
—Revelation 9:3

When the neighborhood rapist appeared in my bedroom at three o'clock one morning, I was sure it had happened before. I recognized the feeling as if it were death. I knew all along it was coming. *Déja vu.* Black, with a hat on. As gently as an ancient, I asked him with all my skills. He assured me he wouldn't hurt my children if I did what he told me. He had been through the house and seen the boys' blond heads on their pillows. What he could see of my room in the dark made him think I was Asian. I could have been. I could have been anything. Geisha woman or goddess.

What must be understood is that he believed me.

A man found a ladder in the basement and broke into my home through a bathroom window. He threatened the lives of my children and would not let me move or turn on a light. And under the circumstances I convinced him he'd made me happy. He promised not to frighten the children. He was lavish with compliments. He said I had a snatch like a sixteen-year-old. All his misery poured forth. He talked about the lousy treatment he'd gotten from women. All they needed was a rod in the right place, he said, then they knew who they were. I consoled him.

He began to give me advice. He told me how careless it was to come home late at night. A carload of friends had driven me to my door about midnight. I'd forgotten my key and had gone around the back, making a lot of noise and calling attention to myself. The porch light was on, he said, so he could see I was wearing a miniskirt. He told me he could break into any house in the neighborhood and what was I doing alone in a place like this, was I on Welfare? I told him I was a high school English teacher and he was very impressed. He told me I must learn to be careful because this whole neighborhood was full of real bad men and they could be watching my house.

Finally he got out of the bed and said good-bye with a sort of wistful sneer. He would go out the back way so as not to wake the children. After I heard the door close I tried to get up. I moved to the end of the bed. Some time later I heard a dog howling somewhere. I tried to get up again. I walked along the wall until I came to the back door. I locked it. I got to the living room and lay down on the sofa. After a while I could hear the birds outside. I found the children buried in their sleeping bags and I unzipped the bags to make sure they had enough air.

It's been a long time now. I sleep in my clothes. I lock my children in their rooms and lock myself in mine. Sometimes I sleep on the sofa next to the phone. The worst thing is, I don't know what he looks like. Black and high cheekbones but that's about all. Every time I see a black man with his profile I have to wonder.

Finally I move. Retrench in a safe neighborhood. It's my own fault. I thought I was a white man. I thought I could live as I liked and the world would love me for being myself. Zen slap. My encounter with the facts. I've got to forget it. It happens all the time.

The nightmare always comes back. It's always the same and it's always different. Sometimes he comes through the walls; sometimes he just drops by with friends and I suddenly know it's him and he was there all the time without my seeing and when I realize this I can't breathe and I'm smothered awake. It's the feeling of suffocation from fear, it's the *I can't scream* dream.

When the police took me to the hospital I was afraid to give my name because my older sister works at the medical records office there and if she found out what had happened I'd never live it down.

1970
(*nightmare three weeks after the rape*)

A tornado crossing the plains is her fallopian tube sucking up the earth and all its creatures into the maelstrom, chewing them gently as it sinks and spreads out into a vagina, collapses into hundreds of little vaginas, all hairy and sweaty and rowdy and punching each other and shrieking and running off into the mountains and leaving their nightgowns thrown on the sand.

She is the only one left now, alone behind a barrel cactus, clinging to the thorns, hiding behind the yellow desert flowers, staring in terror at a mottled gila monster* climbing up the other side of the cactus, his heavy tail sluggishly following him and his hideous tongue lashing from side to side. His eyes do not see. She hisses and spits at him. When the gila monster reaches the hairy hysterical little vagina with her pink nightie on, she jerks and panics into a rabbit held by the ears.

The gila monster's tail erects and swells as he snaps his jaws shut, locked into the little bunny's belly. The monster vomits all the rotten, undigested, lethal muck from his tail through his heart. The poison puts out the sun.

Now the cactus and the sand are burning in the darkness. They are scalded and blistered as radiation begins to rise. There are seashell skeletons rising to the surface of the sea. Hollow bone fragments orbit the earth. Earth herself is honeycombed and porous now. Everything falls away, crumbling like a cracker.

**Gila Monster: A large stout lizard with rough tuberculated skin and a thick tail, found in the arid regions of Arizona, New Mexico, etc. It is pinkish, or dull orange and black in color and of sluggish but ugly disposition. It sometimes obtains a length of about two feet. Also, a closely allied form, H. horridum of Mexico, which has a black head. The bite of these lizards is venomous. Called also beaded lizard. Its digestive system is primitive and most of the food ingested is left to rot in its tail.*

Chris Mandell

THOUGHTS AFTER A RAPE

Strange to think I have been raped
only once;
it felt so familiar,
so similar to things I had hoped were unimportant,
things we do not call rape.

The rape that we call rape
is only one rape,
a rape with perhaps more articulate rage
but still akin to all those vague rapes
that we do not call rape.

The rape that we call rape
has shown me those other rapes
I had thought were nothing.
I have named them now.
I know that rape is no more
than ignorance of the sacred.

There are more rapes than we might suppose.

Kim Addonizio

INSIDE OUT

Today I can't move. Loren was coming over with his truck but it broke down, it will be tomorrow, tomorrow he will come with a truck and move me. I have been living among boxes, boxes in the kitchen which are full of things to put food on, drinks in, there is a box of cookbooks explaining what I am to do. In the bedroom are more boxes, a trunk with very white sheets having a flower pattern, a small accordion file of letters. There is a bag of things. I don't know where I will pack it, maybe in a suitcase. In the bag are private things—a vibrator, lotion, handcuffs, ads for magazines and videotapes showing sexual acts. I masturbate looking at these, though I do not order the magazines or tapes, I look at the very small cunts and cocks and assholes and excite myself.

I have several things to do today, several errands which will take up the time. Time is a problem because there are not always errands to fill it, or there are errands but I can't do them. The biggest problem is leaving the apartment, deciding what clothes are appropriate and actually putting them on and walking down the stairs and into the street. In the street, something could happen. A man might follow me, even in broad daylight, and when I walked faster he would too, and I would turn the wrong way, into a street where there were no more houses, only a big blank warehouse and a store that used to be an upholstery shop. He would pull me into an alley, behind a dumpster, and tell me he was going to kill me. I would have to lie down on some smashed cardboard boxes, my head on the ground, gravel digging into my cheek. I would stare at a paper cup, a medium-sized cup from McDonalds with a plastic lid on top and a clear straw sticking out of it, and listen to the things he said, things I had heard before. Little whore, he said. I can tell you want it. Dirty little girl. I would lie there and not move or speak, even after he got up off of me, even when he was gone.

I have a list of things to do. Today, for example, I have to go to Walgreen's and fill two prescriptions. Walgreen's is one block away, so maybe I will be able to do this. Of course there are people I must pass to get there. I tell myself that they will be nice people, but I don't know. Sometimes it is hard to tell just by looking, sometimes you can be fooled. I will have to find just the right outfit; if it is cold or foggy I can wear the long dark-purple coat from Salvation Army. Also today I have to buy coffee, that is second on my list. The coffee store is around the corner, and the woman who works there is very friendly towards me. I do not have to be nervous about walking in, choosing the right beans, taking out the money and waiting while she grinds them and then giving her the money and taking the change from her hand. In some stores this process of exchanging money is excruciating. If there is a male clerk, even a teenaged boy a couple of years younger than me, I am afraid he will slowly and deliberately brush my palm with the tips of his fingers, and I will not be able to take my hand away. I always try to have pennies and nickels so I can give the correct amount. Walgreen's, the coffee store. This is not too much to ask of myself. Everything is packed and ready to go, there is no reason to stay in today.

I look at myself in the mirror, which has been taken off the wall and leans against an emptied bureau. My thighs are slightly open, dark hairs curl around my cunt. In the mirror I am flat, like a magazine picture. I slip my finger inside where it is wet and warm and contained, and contract the muscles so my finger is held tightly. I throw my head back. Tomorrow Loren will come with his truck, tomorrow he will put his cock where my finger is. Loren says that when we live together, I won't be so afraid. Loren is older, he says he will take care of me. When I curl up in bed he will be there, breathing softly. He will move inside me like this, back and forth. Loren is always careful and patient. He licks me sometimes for what seems like hours, and goes on trying to make me come past the point when he should give up. Finally I push him away, when there is a large wet ring on the sheet from my juices and his saliva. I have explained to Loren that since the rape, I can't come except when I am alone. Masturbating, I rub myself and imagine him fucking me in his loft bed, so close to the ceiling. I see the small cement grains of the ceiling as pores in someone's skin. My orgasm builds and builds, then is over in a second. I have to go to the bathroom. I have to fill two prescriptions at Walgreen's and go to the coffee store. I have to go down the stairs.

Sasha calls. Are you okay, Fran? he says.

Yes, Sasha. But I am going out soon, I have things to take care of. I'm moving in with Loren tomorrow.

Let me come over, Sasha says. I can't work, the piece is going nowhere. I want to see you.

I don't know. I'm on my way out the door.

I have on a sleeveless white jockey undershirt, striped underwear. I have put on purple eyeshadow, mascara, black lipstick. The turquoise stud and the gold monkey in my left ear, a lacquered circle in my right. This is as far as I got, before sitting down and lighting a cigarette. I smoked and looked at myself, looked at the whore in the mirror. I put on a tape Sasha gave me, a performance of some music he wrote, and watched her dance the way they dance at the Lusty Lady, where Sasha took me once. I stood in the small dark booth, and he fucked me from behind while the women swung their hips on the other side of the glass, smiling down at us, moving to loud music under bright stage lights. After smoking the cigarette I felt dizzy and hungry, but there was nothing to eat because I had not been to the grocery store; the grocery store is over three blocks away, so I do not go there often. Also I only get a few items each time— cups of yogurt, pints of one-percent milk, boxes of animal crackers. Small things that will not weigh me down. I get into bed and lie on top of the quilt, listening to the music.

Is that my piece playing in the background? Sasha says.

Yes. I'm just listening to it for the first time. I'm going to lie here and enjoy it for a while.

I thought you were going out.

I am. As soon as your piece is finished.

Please, Fran. Let me come over.

Bring something to eat, then. I haven't been to the store and I'm starving.

Sasha tells me to get on my knees on the kitchen floor and handcuffs me to a leg of the table. He sits cross-legged beside me and feeds me crackers with paté and Camembert, slices of peach, a white chocolate truffle. He feeds me with one hand, and with the other he finger-fucks me. The tape player is on the kitchen table. A string quartet is playing a suite of Thelonius Monk's music. When the first side ends Sasha stands up and flips the tape over.

Do you have any K-Y?

In a box in the bathroom.

My ass is very tight and tensed. I take deep breaths, and he gives me his hand to bite. I bite deeper and deeper, wanting to draw blood. He takes his hand away and slaps me hard on the ass.

Ouch. You're hurting me.

Isn't that what you wanted?

Yes.

I get excited when Sasha hurts me. I don't come, but sometimes I feel as though I might. While we are fucking I feel ashamed of myself; I am betraying Loren with one of his friends. Loren is the one who introduced us, and who suggested that Sasha might want to rent my place so Loren and I could move in together. I do things with Sasha that Loren would probably never think of doing.

Loren is so kind, so patient with me. He wants to protect me, but he can't. He can't be with me every minute. There are always opportunities; this is what I learned as a child. Your mother may have to go work the night shift at the hospital, even if you cry hysterically, even if you wrap your arms around her knees, and your stepfather will pry you off and carry you into your room. I'll give you something to cry about, he'll say. Little whore. Walking around in those shorts. You may have to go to the doctor, and he will take off lunch and pick you up at school and drive you to a parking space in a dark corner of the mall garage, far from the other cars and the people going in and out of the big glass doors. You like it, don't you. Put your mouth on it. A man may follow you for blocks, blocks of ordinary storefronts, flowers on the sidewalk, women pushing strollers, a little boy with a silver balloon. There are places you can't see, holes you might fall into.

Sasha grabs my hair and jerks my head back. God, I love you, he says, and comes.

The men on the first floor are making love, groaning loudly. I wonder which one of them is taking it up his ass—the one who keeps the parrot, or the one with the thin black mustache. I often eavesdrop on my neighbors. I want to know what goes on, what is behind the faces I see in front of the building, faces that smile at me and seem to wish me well. There are airwells, little closed-in alleys, between my building and the ones on each side. The smallest sounds carry. There are also a couple of windows I can see into. In one of them, on the first floor next door, I can see a kitchen sink. Usually I see a woman's hands over the sink, making orange juice in a large pitcher, or scrubbing pans. She and her husband have two little girls, who make a lot of noise playing and then get yelled at by their parents. Late at night I often lie awake and listen, to hear if there might be a small sound from one of the girls, the sound she would make waking up from some dream to feel a hand between her legs, her nightgown being pulled up to cover her face. Sometimes I don't sleep all night.

Through another window, level with my bathroom, I can see a bedroom. I can't see the bed, though I can hear the man and woman making love. Sometimes I catch sight of one of them naked, which excites me, especially if it is the woman. I stare at her breasts, so different from mine—smaller, the nipples pinker, more pointed, like little arrow tips. Her whole body is like cream, her cunt hair very blonde and sparse, her ass too large and veined with stretch marks. I have a pair of binoculars to watch her. Sometimes she stands there for several minutes, apparently looking into a mirror; I see her in profile, leaning forward to peer at her face, then turning sideways so her back is to me and looking over her shoulder. Once the man came up beside her as she was studying herself and rubbed his stiff cock against her, and then pushed inside. I watched them fuck, the man grunting, the woman's head thrown back. I watched her come.

When I see myself fully dressed in the mirror I am reassured that nothing is wrong with me. But really, I am afraid that the person in the mirror is not me, that she is only a picture that moves when I move and disappears when I turn my back. She goes away, where I can't find her, and leaves me here.

Loren always turns out the lights when we make love, but Sasha deliberately exposes me and places me in humiliating positions. When we are out together he will sometimes push me against a wall and kiss me and put his hand inside my coat or down my pants. One night, outside a bar, he fucked me against the post of a street lamp. Even though we had our clothes on, it must have been obvious to anyone who passed what we were doing. I closed my eyes and hid my face in his shoulder, feeling miserable and ashamed and crying softly, but he would not stop. Sasha tells me he is going to turn me inside-out, as if that will help. He doesn't understand that I already feel that way.

One of the men on the first floor has just shouted, *Oh shit, oh shit, oh Jesus.* Sasha left an hour ago, to go back to his piano and work on a score for a ballet. I called Loren, to find out what time he would be coming tomorrow. He wasn't there so I left the question on his machine. I told him I might not be in when he called back, that I had some errands to take care of. I walked around the apartment a couple of times, lay back down on the kitchen floor and masturbated, and then I took a long shower. I imagined the street, the dark places where something could happen, even with people around, even if you covered yourself up. I got dressed, put makeup on.

I just can't do it.

I stand at the window and watch people go by below me. Two women stroll hand in hand, a boy walks a bicycle too big for him. I open the window and sit on the sill, my legs dangling. The day is sunny, starting to cool off a little with a damp breeze. I am on the third floor, it is unlikely that anyone would look up at me. So I am surprised when a man with an unruly golden retriever pulls the dog's leash hard at the corner, stops to wait for the light and glances up. He shades his eyes, looking, and then he waves. I wave back, too startled to withdraw into the safety of the room. I think he must know me. But he isn't one of my neighbors, or anyone I recognize. He's just a stranger. He looks right at me, and smiles, and I realize that he can't really see me, he has no idea who I am.

Bárbara Selfridge

YOUR LOVER WILL NEVER WISH TO LEAVE YOU

(Chinese fortune cookie saying)

The elevator doors close
and I stare up
into the mirrored ceiling.

There's me!

Those pretty black-lashed eyes, that shy smile
I am seduced
by the line of my breasts, so close
to the soft oval of my face—

(I know, I know! The pose distorts;
the real me is somewhat overweight, somewhat
moon-faced, and knows it isn't true.)

— but you are, I say.
You're the prettiest office temp
in the whole city. You can't help
but set hearts on fire.

And when I laugh, unbelieving,
the woman in the mirror laughs back,
falls down in love with me.

— *He loves you as much as he can,*
but he can not love you very much.

I believe fortune cookies
when they're heartless
and collect the slips in my purse:

— *Courage is your greatest present need.*
— *If your desires are not extravagant, they will be granted.*
— *Watch your relations with other people, be reserved.*
— *For better luck you will have to wait until winter.*

And if a man asks for my picture,
I give him a snapshot
more romantic than I am.

It doesn't look like you, my mother says.

The eyes look more purple, the skin
less blemished than the truth,
and in order to achieve the distortion that I love,
I've thrown my face
forward, almost into the lens,
and upset the kitten on my lap.

It is a picture of Whiskers, back
when she was a kitten, being squashed.

It looks like that actress you hate,
my best friend says. *What's her name?*

I answer them laughing, tell
the secret of my elevator vanity,
and then my mother and best friend
both want copies. I feel their words—
the way Barbara thinks she looks—
written on the photo's other side,
and I want it back.

The man who couldn't bear,
he said, to let me go,
has that picture, found again
after it slipped a while behind another
in his scrapbook,

and sometimes when he looks at it,
or changes lovers,
he calls me up.

I can't bear, he says, to let you go.

And there's no mention of the attempted rape
the night we broke up, no picture of me
barefoot, running out into the street,

no echo of his phone calls:
I'm going to fuck you up.
FUCK YOU UP!

No, it's just him saying the sweetest words he knows,
speaking to that sweet-faced photo,
me on the party line, me listening in
while my bowels turn liquid.

(And why didn't I try that then?
Why not shit in my pants
when my wrists were trapped?)

Someone bought a fortune-telling fish
for a penny: a thin blue fish, plastic,
made in Taiwan, and every time
that fish lay on my palm,
it stood on its head.

The key explained:
that meant FALSE. False, the fish said.
False, false, false.

Laura Goodman

SOUND OF SPEED

My name is Felice Durbin, I am 22 years old, and I was raped. *is this the way they want it i have practiced* Yes sir, I understand: the facts.

Okay. I walked out my front door, down the walk, out into the street, and stood there in my nightdress. Yes sir, until the police car came. *was a long time i think till they came though when i first went out there a car came right away and stopped big car but not new almost like one daddy drives ma'am he said* I didn't know him, didn't think even for a second that it was Daddy driving up. *do you need help* Oh no, ma'am! Not Daddy! My daddy? No, no. Carl, and I know Carl. Yes, I know you know Carl, too. *i've been raped i practiced i said to him through his open car window he kind of reminded me of my daddy some too grey-haired and the same glasses maybe even a little bit nicer smile opened his door and one foot boot black boot stepped out help* Course it was. It was Carl all right. Carl Durbin. *i practiced my husband raped me i said because carl had just got done doing it to me that way and the stuff was still stinging way up inside but had started running down my legs too as i said it i practiced he swallowed air* No ma'am, it wasn't the first time. *work it out honey car man said and his smile dried up like mud* Six months, a year maybe. *what they think i don't know who did what to me i know carl and that the car man was someone i don't know wish it had been daddy in the car help except i don't know if i could tell all the things to him and daddy hadn't ever much liked carl anyway i don't think it stung it still stings always* A lot. *car man shifted quick back into drive boot and i heard his door slam as his tires took him away fast like all the cars on our street go fast even when they're not i can hear the sound of their speed* It's gotten worse, is what. *my husband raped me* And more. Yes, often. *raped me that bottle up inside the stinging scarf* More often. It's not right. *i practiced my husband raped me my husband me raped*

he drove off and left me but it wasn't unpleasant alone in the street mild the black air in the night and there was a clear cut half moon shining over my head and carl was lying asleep on the floor i knew he wasn't dead But I felt a little free. What? Oh no sir, not that, not doing it, not with him, you only feel bad. *stinging stinking and pain and sad and no hope and cars speeding by my husband raped me* Standing out in the street, I mean, after, free. *breeze going through my nightdress and drying me off free as the breeze i thought and i liked that in french my name means happy or something felice i used to think i was i used to think id go to france someday and meet a french girl named happy* But I knew it couldn't last and that I had to get freer. *scissors they don't know don't want to* From him, Carl. Yes, Carl, and the things. *they're writing this down whatever i say but i don't see that they believe me carl's one of them they protect their own i know he says it often enough no hope for you girlie he says from inside his laugh over and over me time after time it hurts no hope* Things, yes. *scarf which was so pretty but even though it looks the same the pretty is gone siphoned off a little at a time ugly me carl hurting things* That he did. To me. *carl if he was explaining they'd get it cause he can talk and make people see things his way and he's one of them theirs he'd even maybe put in about the bottle and the scarf and the scissors and my asking him not to begging he'd say was part of it like we agreed but not how much it hurts and inside me stings the stuff inside the bottle inside stings me* The bottle? *into me bees stinging millions of sharp blood stingers stinging* Yes, sir, I did. Back of the head. *Carl's not dead I'm not so lucky if i put in these things into what i say things will they believe me him yes but me* No sir, I don't know who called the police. *they aren't very nice they don't believe me I'm not one of them so they don't understand* He did things to me. *scissors the scarf maybe they wont even believe about the stuff in the bottle the bottles on that table over there they don't know what he did they know what i did cause i told them* Ugly things. Please. *believe me unspeakable things Carl*

cars all the time swooshing by the house out in the street tires carrying fast cars by going fast slow going sounding fast sounding speed car lights on the wall in the dark and what he did what he always did I'm your husband i have my rights Serious head injury? I didn't mean to, only to stop him. *hello my name is happy she would tell me but i don't really hear her voice anymore because of the tires speed sound*

Two years, yes, two years ago we got married. *felice please i love you so please please marry me please girl nobody ever begged me for anything like that not even candy when i was little and no one else had any but me* Not at first, no ma'am. *at first i didn't know i was no good i never had before you just lay down he told me one night and ill show you he sucked my breasts rough like he always did even from the beginning with his teeth and rammed me hard with his thing and i heard the speed of tires on asphalt even back then and he finished right off but he didn't stop he diddled me with his fingers in and out and all around and everything got slippery with his cum and i began to heave up the first time for that and it felt good and he sucked my breasts again but gentle gentle that night for once then he licked them and didn't bite them and i got a rhythm and i beat myself into his fingers and thought about france and the girl named happy a lot back then and i came too for the first time see he said see i told you it was good now you know your part*

Stood there. Waiting, I guess. *i heard them panting before i saw them and they came out from behind krammers fitzer shrubs* I don't know what I was waiting for. *i practiced my husband practiced raped me it in my head till i knew practiced every time my husband* Help? *two dogs one big one littler panting and moving in jerky steps tail to tail looking around and backwards at each other and it took me a minute my husband to realize they were locked together the way dogs get when they mate dogs don't mate unless they want to both of them* Dogs were in the bushes; they came running out. *ill never go to France and meet the girl who lives there she imagines me with her name no hope*

It was dark, and I don't know if anyone saw me. Only the two dogs. *in the beginning he used to ask me if i was in the mood feeling sexy did i want to play and i did thought i was doing it right what he wanted always to the sounds of the cars in the street their speed i could hear going fast going slow going going but he said i didn't get it it wasn't right not for a long time now has he asked me anything he rams me he sucks and spits on my breasts and bites me like he never gets enough for dinner or like he hates me but he doesn't he says he knows i like it this way because i always do my part but not the scissors scarf bottle stinging the poisoned babies blood sometimes inside out outside in not those things they are not my part* I didn't see anyone after the man in the car until the police came Just the dogs. *walking sideways and looking back at each other like they were ready for it to be over i have my rights he would say like growling I'm your husband what does it matter no hope for you girlie no one will believe you nobody cares*

Then I started walking towards the corner. 'Scuse me? Where to? *france maybe* Oh, I don't know where I thought I was going. *i knew like those dogs i was walking towards something and away at the same time*

Adam David Miller

YOU'LL NEVER KNOW HOW MUCH

Kinesha walked in one evening after work, no greeting, no nothing. Just said, "Benny, I'm leaving. I want out."

I was waxing the Trans-Am, on the right front fender.

I looked up, said, "Bye," and turned back to the waxing. My wife sometimes likes her little joke.

Without a word she walked into the fourplex. We lived on the second floor.

Then it hit me what she had said. *You have got to be kidding.* I called up to the window, "Neesha, you come back out here."

After awhile, she stuck her head out, "No, Benny, you come up here."

Upstairs, I found her putting clothes into two open suitcases on the bed. Socks and underwear in neat piles. I noticed the walk-in closet was almost empty.

"Where are the rest of your things?"

"I've already moved most of my stuff over to my new place. I see you haven't noticed."

I slammed the largest suitcase shut and sat on it.

"Will you puleeze tell me what the hell's going on!"

"Nothing's going on. *Nuh thing.* Now please get up off my suitcase. I want to get over there before dark."

"So you've planned all this—"

"Yep. Right under your nose, with your eyes wide closed. You said 'bye,' now let me go."

She seemed close to crying.

Not knowing what else to do, I slid off the suitcase, grabbed her by the shoulders and shook her. She looked at me, her eyes steady and bright. I was struck by their brownness, like her skin. She closed them and lowered her head."

"You're bigger than me. You know that, don't you? You're hurting my shoulders."

"O motherfuck!" I threw her on the bed and stumbled into the bathroom, locking the door behind me. I sat on the commode for I don't know how long. I could hear faint movements in the apartment, the flap-slide of mules then the click-tap of heels. Sharp snap of suitcases, one, the other. I imagined the shutting of the door down the long hall. Silence.

After what seemed like the longest time, I looked up. It was dark outside. I noticed for the first time how the faint light hit the trees, giving them a glossy blackness.

I found her note pinned to my pillow: "I want to make something out of myself. You don't. And you don't want me to." On the phone nightstand were keys to the apartment, her key to the Trans-Am, the address and phone number to her new place. Not too far away.

I crumpled the note and started to throw it in the wastebasket. As I drew back my hand I lowered it. Took the note and smoothed it out. Put it on the nightstand near the keys and her new address. Started to lift up the phone. Put the receiver back. Sat down on the bed. Tried to get up and couldn't. Laid on my side and curled up in a ball.

The weight of twelve years of marriage had come crashing down on me and I was paralyzed. Couldn't even cry out.

My life had been going pretty damned good up to then. I had my job. Had an AA degree and was thinking about finishing college. Had the only woman I ever really wanted, new black Trans-Am, state-of-the-art sights and sounds, friends. Sitting on top of the world. Boom! the shit hits the fan and I'm covered with it.

True, I wasn't going anywhere. I know, I mean, but where is there to go?

Line supervisor at the Base. Since I was evening shift, I was pulling down some good bread. Had a job as long as they have wars, right? For damned sure we're always gonna have wars. Human nature. And we know the good old U. S. of A. will be right in the middle of them, from now on in.

True, Kinesha had been pushing of late: "Why don't you do something more with that degree, something you can be happy with?"

"Now, hey baby, who says I'm not happy at the Base? Sure I bitch about the job. We all do. You don't like the money I'm making? Aren't we stashing some away for that house you wanted?"

True, we'd had a chance for a house six years before. Nice two-bedroom on a quiet street. Almost closed the deal when I cold-watered it. Just wasn't the right time for me. Too chancey. I told Kinesha so.

She didn't say anything much. She wanted that house. Her folks had a lovely home.

"I'm making money too, you know."

That's right, she'd always had some kind of little chump change job. Clerk at Macy's. Bookkeeper for a buddy of mine who was in real estate. Don't know what happened there. Now she's secretary in a government office.

Studying dance when we got married. Would've gone on with it, I suppose. Talked about it once in awhile. But we both knew that you can't make any money being a dancer, unless you're someone high up, like that Agnes de Mille they show on TV. So she let it slide.

Kinesha's parents hadn't wanted me to marry their daughter. Was back when boys from Nam were eating crow. I was caught in the same trick bag like the rest even though I wasn't a combat vet. Nobody shot at me and I didn't shoot at nobody. Viet Cong didn't even know I was there. Thank the good Lord for that.

But Kinesha's folks, especially her mother, held Nam against me.

Had to give Kinesha credit, she stood up to them. Just as stubborn as her mother.

"Daddy came back from a war and you married *him*."

"That was Korea. This one is different."

"War is war. What's the big deal?"

Her mother closed the argument. Every time after one of these flareups, she'd clamp her jaws and take on a look I've seen on Kinesha.

She was disappointed when I didn't wake up in the middle of the night screaming, "The Viet Cong are coming," like some of the vets she saw on TV.

Hell, I didn't even do drugs. After awhile she let up on me. My vet's status got me points for the job on the Base. That helped some.

Course, like all couples, especially when you're first married, we had our fights. Fight and make love, fight and make love some more. Then the fights stopped and the love-making slowed to a trot. Not that we didn't do our share, but you know how it is after a couple of years. You kinda get used to one another. No surprises.

At thirty there abouts Kinesha began to pick up a little weight—not too much, I don't like skinny women. But you know how women are, when they think they're getting on in age.

We were watching TV one night, one of those dance galas. Where they've got foxy young chickies prancing over the stage and shaking it for all they're worth. Except for sports, I don't watch TV much. That night I had my eyes glued to the set.

"Man, you see how they toss those girls around. Sliding them through their legs and pulling them back. Damn!"

Kinesha didn't say anything. Just went out and started banging dishes around in the kitchen. She acted like I said something about her. Didn't have anything to do with her.

About a week later I found a package in the mail from the local spa.

Then there was the beach picnic. Four couples, all from the Base. Wine and beer, cards, volley ball, picnic snacks from Fox's deli.

After food and some of the drinks, we guys left the wives, gathered a little way off, spread a blanket for some five-card stud. The women settled back to sun and beat their gums.

Guys talk eventually got around to the wives. Naturally each man had to clarify his situation to his advantage, right? We all had good wives. I, being the youngest, went last: "What I want, my wife wants. What I say do, she does. Go when I say go, come when I say come. What more can a man want than that?"

I won hands down. "Man, you've got the money and the glory." I had gone seven dollars up. We slapped hands all around.

About three next morning, I got up to pee and found Kinesha awake.

"You were right, you know, Benny."

"What do you mean?"

"That stuff on the beach."

"I didn't even know you girls were listening."

"We all heard."

"Oh, now, come on Neesha, you know how guys are. Get together and brag. Stud fighting. My thing is bigger than yours, that kind of bullshit—"

She was looking at me in a funny way, with a look I'd never seen on her before.

"You were right. It's been that way with us. When I married you I thought you were god's gift to woman. And we made so many grand promises. *I'll be good to you baby, to the best that I know how. My Queen.* I would have walked on nails if you had told me to."

"Aw, you take that stuff too seriously. Just guys shooting the bull. Girl, go back to sleep."

"Hold me, Benny, I'm scared."

I held her. Her body was hard as a rock, and as cold.

Two months later she left that note.

I got over the first shock. I no longer hung around the apartment, like I was looking for something—or somebody. Walking the rooms. It seemed like such a big place, so empty suddenly.

But deep down, I wasn't worried over much. We had too much going for us. Too much behind us. Twelve years.

She still worked in the state office buiding and lived over on Thornhill. Not far. I had her phone number. Called it once. Her answering machine had a man's voice. Damn! Scared the hell out of me, until I realized it was her father.

When I drove by, there was never any sign of man. So far so good. She'd be back.

I worked my way to the bottom of my underwear drawer and there was that printed sheet: Anonymous, from a Chinese tea box, "...He who risks nothing, achieves nothing. He who is afraid of change is afraid of life."

I felt Kinesha standing at my elbow. Could feel her body heat, her breath. I desperately wanted her, I wanted to be with her, wherever she might be going. I'd even do my time walking on nails, if it'd help.

But her heat faded. All that was left in the room was a cold breeze.

Martha W. Ostheimer

CUT OUTS

Epoxied to the back porch
the colors of another day,
like a lovely little back drop

for what are you doing with your life now,
are wearing themselves out.
And the traffic stuck on the bridge

as another good take on desire
replacing: terrible screaming,
what you did today. The radio

beating up another woman exclusively
in a 911 bulletin cuts out with
I love him like no one could believe that.

Like night blooming cereus the greatest
of great expectations or any woman's life:
only never to be beaten.

Some smoke stacks and every other thing
disappearing, I think you say *handsome,*
he is really handsome

what she should have said on the radio.
Flood lights sputtering to come on
get the parking lot downstairs and Norman's car

sloppy with the top half-up where he left it in focus
like any other clip on the tv.
A pack of blackbirds just off the wire

for exaggerated beauty, and how I am
all reverence, a couple bourbons down now—
the soliloquy of a bruised up friend

going sage on the attributes of suffering
and the seizing and singing to Norman's car
the tow truck was doing

that ended up the same way— the same thing
over and over until you're sick of it—
is exactly as you left me, my darling.

Lisa Martinović

STARING AT THE CEILING WISHING IT WERE OVER

you don't want to do it in the first place
you're tired
it's been a rough week
and hot, so goddamn hot
no A/C in the apartment
lotta fleas, though
and mosquitoes
heat makes your bites swell up to where you look
    vaguely infectious

you're hot and itching and tired
and he comes over and strips down to boxer shorts
in his opening sentence
He plops down on your tiny bed so now
your sheets are gonna smell like cigarettes and rancid deodorant
and oh well you lie down with him
though you can't imagine exerting
the effort it would take to actually come
and you're depressed, too
so you aren't capable of even *envisioning* ecstasy
but he's a good man and it's been nearly a week so
he must be dying on the vine, right?
you offer a blow job to which he replies
Baby, if I ever turn down a blow job
I want you to take me out and shoot me in the head
You suck
he bucks
on and on till your jaw starts to ache
because you've got this problem where you
clench with the force of vice grips in your sleep
you've got some theories about the secret object of all
    that gnashing
but right now you only know it hurts when he doesn't
    come soon enough
so when you've had all the tonsil banging you can endure
you hop on top
straddling his turgid, throbbing, erect and yearning blah blah blah
Thank you, baby, he moans

Sure, sure, you think, just hurry up and come
which of course he doesn't
and all your heroic acrobatic attempts to conclude this ordeal
result only in leg cramps
so you maneuver the heaving animal onto your chest
—let him do the work
he groans and pumps
strains and bumps
and by now you're staring at the ceiling wishing it were over
cuz it's starting to hurt
you're getting dry and sore
and the fucking KY jelly is at his house
sweat is dripping off his nose into your face
you stare *real hard* at the ceiling
you wish *real bad*
it were over
and it's sad
so sad
because you know you're not alone
you know there are thousands of women
at this very moment
maybe millions of women
being pumped and thrusted into
millions of women
and me
staring at the ceiling
wishing it were over
and wondering if he'll ever notice that we're busy
planning dinner
worrying about the rent
deciding on the color of the new drapes

Jeff Walt

WHERE WE LIVED

If I could have looked at myself in the mirror
maybe I would still be there wandering from
room to room with a cup of water, almost
drowning the ivy because *I* was thirsty. Maybe

I'd still be breaking the china, piece by piece,
because I thought you loved the pattern more
than me. Or perhaps I'd reach toward the ceiling
again and grasp the chandelier's hot bulb

until the smell of flesh and smoke suffused the air.
But God kept coming down to us.
Wasn't it odd that *He* came to us?
Like when I awoke from dreaming about *The End*:

your place next to me in bed was empty and on TV
the Spanish station was playing and there He was
working that man's lips, repeating
¿Como se dice love? *¿Como se dice* love?

I understood his question. I understood
how a room can tighten like a fist.
I stumbled through fear of being left alone,
through an entire house to the lit kitchen

where not even the wooden table with its old
black cuts looked familiar.
I said that the objects I love most
I do not need; that what should be in my heart

is taped inside a box in the closet.
And in the end—the real end, now—I said,
I am leaving with only a rind of my heart.
The melodrama made us laugh as I backed out the door.

Laughter fell down that dark mahogany staircase.
In the streets I laughed at the common world:
nervous pigeons cooing, birds dancing on wires
and a woman in spiked heels walking her dog.

Suddenly my heart began a great song
and in the middle shut up. Lay quiet
for a while. I did chores with that sad heart;
we lived as people do

inside a frail body without chairs
or a deck of cards for company. We slept
inside our heavy breathing without a wall
to separate us.

IN TRANSIT

Steam rises
from piss—
the tile floor
of a bus station bathroom.
We communicate
like deaf mutes
with simple gestures:
Your wink and nod call
me into a rusty stall,
into your corporate aftershave,
to my knees.
I am grateful as you open
the trench coat,
unzip the dark
banker's pants.
I quietly suck
the mystery
from the wellspring
inside you,
words exchanged
by touch.
You board a bus
for Downingtown
as I wait in transit
knowing
you could never love
me in the bright-lit,
public rooms
of the world.

Nancy Casey

LIFELINES

On an August Friday, as twilight darkened the corners of my kitchen, I lit the lanterns, cranked a sheet of paper into the typewriter and began a letter to Joe's mother, Babs.

Can't get you off my mind, I typed. Both babies had fallen asleep early and I was alone. *I just finished cutting up four huge heads of cabbage "as thin as a dime" like the recipe says, then I sprinkled a heaping teaspoon of salt over each quart of cabbage as I packed it "gently but firmly" into a crock. I hope it turns into sauerkraut. You should see this kitchen. It is strewn with cabbage scraps and dirty dishes. I dug two sacks of beets this afternoon, and they are waiting on the counter to be peeled and pickled. But first I am taking a break. And I have to remember to milk at 8:00.*

I was responding to a recent letter in which she had blurted her frustration with being confined to a tin-walled house, nursing an ill-humored heart patient who refused to be left alone long enough for her to visit her family, and who ridiculed her for wanting to. At any time, though, he could die, and she was afraid.

I stoked the cook stove, set the cauldron of beets over the fire, then went outside to catch the goats and walk them up the lane to the milking stand. Darkness settled, I massaged Gardenia's soft, heavy udder, and did not know how to open the conversation I longed to have with Babs. The words I needed were not used to inquire about a person's life.

I carried Babs in a remembered photograph that was part companion and part dream. The photo is distant, faded, as all casually stored snapshots from the 50's are. There is a woman and a shack. She is Joe's mother. I see the isolation because I know it, miles from neighbors. In the foreground are small things, children perhaps, or their toys. Rural, pre-television poverty did not have to be desperate. No doubt there were chickens and a garden where the moist nights of warm summers made for the opulent swelling of tomato flesh.

We didn't have nothing then, she said. *We made toys and drew pictures.* This is the life that Joe and I were recreating for our children.

Her husband, who towered over her in other photos, was not in this picture. Much of the time he was off running his eighteen-wheeler across the country on 2-lane interstates. If they didn't get their things out of the yard before he pulled in, he ran them over. They only cowered from his rage when he was there, so it was possible for their lives to seem like this picture until a heart attack that almost killed the big truck driver turned him into a garage mechanic and the whole family found a new life in town.

Savor these moments hard, Babs always said in her letters, and I did. She wrote of how the work and exhaustion of her time with tiny children made it speed by that much faster. The days once seemed so endless, yet they had all slipped away from her.

I connected my life to her past. I tried to feel moments enough for us both, and tapped the rhythms of my days on a manual typewriter in the corner of the kitchen, filling my letters to her with the smell of wood smoke, the golden rose tint of evening, and the sounds of chickens, children, and insects that filtered through the dusty heat of midday. My body, like hers in the photo, was to grow sinewy and strong under the cotton print dress.

Once Joe told me about a session in therapy when he suddenly remembered himself crouched behind the bedroom door; his father was lashing at him with a belt and each of them was screaming for the other one to stop. *I already know that much,* I wanted to tell her, but it was not my place to say so. *What did he do to you? Tell me how you coped with the rage.* If we could discuss it, I was sure she would tell me that things settle down, that you grow old together, and that what becomes important is not how you have hurt each other, but what you have shared.

The frenzied yipping of a pack of running coyotes poured over the hillside and filled the draw. I carried the milk toward the reassuring glow emanating from the windows of the shake-shingled house against the trees. I climbed the uneven steps of the creaking porch. The soft slam of the screen door announced my return to my kitchen.

Once the milk was strained and cooling under a damp towel, the beets were ready to be plunged into cold water, then skinned and sliced. There were jars to sterilize, lids to count, spices to measure and mix. The familiar dance of canning began, and hours passed before I could sit at the typewriter again to report to Babs about the way the lantern light gleamed in the rows of ruby-violet jars lined on the counter. The lids pinged intermittently as they sealed.

I can't stop thinking of how alone you are feeling, I wrote, and then fell short of connecting her loneliness to mine. *I should be thankful that my biggest problems are that the baby goats climb all over my car, the hen house needs cleaning, my hair is dirty, there is only one clean diaper left, and I can't think about washing the dirty ones until this kitchen has been overhauled...*

There was no innocuous sentence I could type which would naturally lead to talking about the rest. Joe came home, the letter ended, and I never found a way to ask her if her most terrible times were also in the dark.

Even now, the memory makes me wide-eyed when I return to myself sitting upright, naked in the center of the mattress, bedclothes swirled around my thighs, staring at the chimney. Downstairs he rages that he hates me, his curses punctuated with thumping furniture and shattering glass. The freezing tingle begins to grow, tinsel-like, from the base of my spine. Clawing up and radiating across my shoulders, it ascends the neck, covers the scalp, clangs inside the head, and engulfs all but a tiny mask of face in electric silver and white.

The clear voice which often narrates or gives orders when I am frozen penetrates from behind and slightly above my right eye. *This,* it observes with a calmness that is not soothing, *is what fear feels like. This feeling is fear.*

I inhabit a cold, lucid moment that extends forever. I try to make myself invisible and wait to see how bad it will get before it is over.

Afterward, maybe, he will be sorry, but will claim that there is nothing that can be done. A long time ago this terrible rage went inward and it nearly destroyed him. He is learning to get it out. Someday he will be rid of it.

When spring began to run fresh in the creeks and the air in the valley was laden with the moisture of thaw, the snow on the mountain would still be thigh-high and each day seemed bathed more in darkness than daylight. Driving the Minnaloosa Valley road home with groceries, I would review my options, which seemed like no options at all. Hadn't we made a commitment to each other? I reached inward deeper and deeper to find love and compassion with which to sustain myself. How else could we emerge together on the other side of these hard times? To back out now would signal that I no longer believed that we should support each other. It would mean that I was not strong, and that I had failed. Also, I had nowhere to go, and if I told him to leave, he would return in the dark and only babies and stars would hear me call for help.

I drove the curves and swells on the soft gravel road, bathed in despair. The voice that watched and sometimes gave directions reminded me that there was another option. *You could always die,* it pointed out clearly and without judgment. I understood the connection between suicide and humiliation.

From the pair of car seats behind me came mostly the sound of thumbsucking. Occasionally one child mimicked the other's exclaimed observations. What hope would there be for these children if their mother did not care enough about them to live?

Sometimes I would clutch the wheel and scream so hard I could taste blood in my throat.

The neighbor drove up one morning with a message for Joe to phone home, an emergency. The heart attack, no doubt, that had threatened to claim his father any minute for the last fifteen years. But when Joe called, his father answered the phone. The emergency was Babs. She was in the State Hospital. She had tried to kill herself. He had been frantic for weeks because every time he took his eyes off of her, even if she went to the bathroom alone, she would try and do it. Pills, razors, rat poison? He didn't say.

In the first letter that came from her afterwards, she wrote that she was choosing to live, despite the hell and pain that her therapist assured her she would have to climb back through. For months she did little but crochet and scrawl out the story of her life on yellow, lined newsprint with ball-point pen and no margins, folding the pages to fit envelopes stamped and addressed to the four winds.

Many of them came to us, filled with faded black and white stories, lantern-lit and dark, from a Carolina share-cropper childhood. She picked tobacco and cotton for a penny a pound. Her father's name was southern and square, something like Carson. He gambled or drank, maybe both, finally disappeared. Once, he spit tobacco into a pot of beans bubbling for her 8 brothers and sisters, and her mother bashed his head in with the stove lid, the only time she ever raised a hand to him. During the war, she and her sisters came home from the factories where they worked and sewed each other dresses to wear to dances on the weekends.

Months later, she wrote about her relationship with her husband, telling how there were many reasons to blame him and push him away. He was still trying to hold her back, criticizing her for how she spent her time, discouraging her from going out. But in the hospital, he was the one beside her bed, not her children or her siblings. There he sat, hunched and worried, his presence pleading with her to decide not to die. This man could have abandoned her, but he didn't. She would not abandon him.

Her words gave me hope and strengthened my faith in the importance of forgiveness and the depth of love. I hadn't learned any other interpretations for such incidents, nor recognized the pattern of this practiced dance, the one where the charade of tenderness and promise bids you to call in your symptoms, capitulate, and forgive. The man at her deathbed was a semi-invalid with no friends who probably didn't even know how to cook. What else would he have done besides plant his elbows on his thighs and look broken?

I didn't know if it was possible to consume enough beer and valerian to actually die, but one afternoon when the season was again dipping towards winter, Joe was on the living room floor when I came home. His sleep was deep, his breathing soft, and the smells were unmistakable. He often threatened to kill himself, but his talk that morning made me realize that this time he was more serious. He had asked me to call a doctor friend of his who worked at a psychiatric hospital in Coeur d'Alene. Before I left to do so, he brought me the shotgun and told me to hide it from him. Getting himself slogged out on the floor like that while he was waiting for me to come home, however, was just a stupid obstacle that he threw in the path of my help. *If you can wake up and walk, get in the car.*

Had I not been able to rouse him, or had he passed out again, the winding ride north on I-95 would have been easier. As I drove, he ranted from the back seat about poets on the steps of the nuthouse, poets and artists, all that genius on the steps of the nuthouse, misunderstood. I pictured Grecian columns behind wide steps flanked by stone lions where juvenile punks lounged in black leather and sunglasses with cigarettes rolled into their shirt sleeves. There would be plenty of time for creative jive on the nuthouse steps once he had done his time inside.

By then I was too well-acquainted with the limits of my pain tolerance to have reserves from which to generate compassion. This excursion was merely inevitable, distinguishable from all the other episodes only because it was more extreme, and as such, perhaps it carried the promise of transformation. The logistics of his psychiatric treatment would be exhausting for me, but still not as draining as the uncertainty and desperation of wondering if he would ever realize he needed help. This could be an important change. Perhaps we had truly traveled to the edge and were about to cross the threshold to the other side.

These were the things I was thinking as I waited for the gas tank to fill in Worley. My spirits lifted. The challenges ahead were difficult, but straightforward. I could do this. Washing the windshield, I marched around the front of the car to the tune of the *Sorcerer's Apprentice,* which had begun singing itself in my head. When I caught the eye of the miserable creature staring out from the back seat, the look I flashed was capable, almost cheerful.

When I got back into the car he was revived and fueled, furious that I couldn't conceal my delight at having him dispatched and out of the way. No doubt I had some dirty hippie waiting to take his place once he was locked up. He pumped venom into his tirade on nigger-fuckers and disease-infested cunts, the one with the oozing puss, old cum, juju and blood. I had heard it so many times that I only winced on account of the kids. In a couple of hours we would all be delivered.

By the time we reached Coeur d'Alene, he was slumped and silent. We sat in a line of left-turning cars, waiting for our chance to dart across the three lanes of oncoming rush hour traffic. I could see the wide, quiet streets of the hospital zone.

The car door slammed and I jumped. Twisting in my seat, I caught only glimpses of him dodging through the stream of traffic behind me. I managed a U-turn and caught up with him pacing in an empty parking lot beneath the sign that displayed the names of the CPAs, insurance agents, and credit counselors who had all gone home. I hopped out of the car, calming myself, and trying to formulate the words that would coax him back.

He aimed a finger at me, growled that he would kill me if I took one step closer, and I believed him. Who, in all this traffic speeding past, would notice, much less pull over for a rescue, if he began choking me, or threw me to the asphalt and started kicking in my face?

Walking back towards the car, I shrugged to the expectant faces of the kids. "He wants to stay here." We drove to a grocery store so I could find them something to eat. From there I called some friends who lived in a neighboring valley and admitted that I was afraid to go home. Later, at their house, after all the children were asleep, I said it out loud for the first time. *I don't care anymore if he kills himself. If that is what is going to happen, I am ready to get it over with.*

In the morning before anyone else awoke, I slipped out and drove over the mountain alone to see what was happening at home. The horses needed to be fed and the other animals let out. As I pulled up, Joe's face was looking down from the kitchen window, so drained and dispirited that I knew I did not need to be afraid. Quietly, he let me drive him to the hospital the next day.

After a few days, however, he decided against completing a 4-week treatment program for severe depression. Two doctors vouched that the isolation of our unorthodox lifestyle was the primary cause of his condition, so we began making plans to move to a small college town. There, he found a job as a newspaper reporter, and I found the reassuring presence of other women, a telephone, and the police.

Even though moving was supposed to be the first step in solving all of our problems, he kept on talking about killing one or the other of us, and I lost hope that he would ever confront and heal the wounds of his past. People I had not known for very long said things to me like, *Any time, Nancy. Day or night. If you need me, call me.*

It was a Wednesday night that I told him that if he didn't move out by the weekend, I would. He said he would kill himself before that happened.

"Fine," I said. "Just don't make a mess. These children don't deserve to see you splattered all over some wall."

My insolence increased his agitation. His rage seemed more dangerous than ever, all of it focused on me. I had never felt so afraid of him. I slipped out the front door, intending to walk a few blocks and wait for some calm to return.

Not far from home, I paused and tried to gather my thoughts. Had he settled down yet? Should I walk to a friend's house? Were the kids okay? It was always me he went after, never them. A passing police car slowed on the other side of the street. No doubt I looked strange— shivering, no coat, standing still in the middle of the block at 2 AM. I was thinking about what to say if they were going to stop, when a searchlight blinded me.

"Throw down your weapon, and put your hands in the air!" boomed a megaphone voice. Squinting, hands high, head averted, I stumbled toward the source of the light, ready to explain that they had made a mistake. They were responding to a call from a man whose wife was lurking in the neighborhood with a gun, threatening to kill him. The address that they were checking out was mine. Two more squad cars slipped into position at either end of the block. Backup. *Domestic violence with guns is the most dangerous kind.*

It was not hard to convince them that I was the least dangerous of the two of us. They convinced me to leave home that night. I heard Joe shouting and swearing at the two officers who escorted him to one end of the block while I went inside, swaddled the two sleeping children in their blankets and carried them to the car.

I returned home in the morning, detached and curious. I had run out of ideas for imagining what might happen next. The destruction that I stepped into when I opened the front door gave testimony to how much rage can be bottled inside a human being before it explodes. Anything that could be lifted had been hurled— potted plants, mattresses, dishes, jars full of fruits and vegetables. Bookcases were up-ended, and everything made of wood— tables, guitars, picture frames— had been splintered. The phone was ripped out of the wall, and all my clothes were in the garbage can.

I have experienced moments when uncontrollable rage boils and surges up through my chest and overtakes me, but this rampage must have taken hours. Did he move methodically from one room to the next? Did he have to make a special trip to the toolbox to get the hammer he used to destroy my piano? I wonder how he knew he was finally spent, if he collapsed and slept in the wreckage, what he saw in the morning when he awoke, what he stepped over when he showered, dressed, and went to his job.

I was shocked but grateful. What an illusion was the control I thought I always had over our situation! I had merely worked ever-so-hard to soothe and ignore all of the warning signs of this inevitable explosion. I felt lucky to have escaped alive and unharmed.

A judge issued an Order for Protection, and the police enforced it. A small army of women materialized around me to clean my house, lend me furniture, and stand rock-solid beside me. Babs wrote that I was high-minded and bad, that no woman has the right to separate a man from his children, and that unless I got the punishment I deserved I would be free to drive some other humble soul to the terrible state in which I had left Joe. When Joe's father was in the hospital for the final time, my daughter cried inconsolably because her grandfather was going to die without ever having seen her.

Will I ever tell a version of this story so complete that it is free of accusation and bitterness? That is what I seek. How else can I reclaim my old optimism and believe that love has any power at all? Each time I travel in memory to the years that I spent on that lovely wooded hillside, a dark and massive sadness settles heavy into my chest. There will never be enough comfort. Even so, I reach into that place again and again, because it seems that if I can touch that blackness just right, it will turn into a bird, and I can let it go.

Rachel Loden

A FALLING WOMAN

Sometimes
a woman
falls through her family
and is lost
even beyond
the keep of daughters
and no man
can cross the border of that darkness

Sometimes a woman breaks
and her wild words
can weave no cover;
they are no warmth
at night when she is shuddering...

Sometimes a woman
waits and spins
beneath the fatherland
and no one's song
is sweet enough
to lure her home

Jayne Relaford Brown

WAR ZONE

For a moment I was there with you,
the night I woke up, trapped.
You covered every inch of me
and pinned me to the bed.
Your heart a burst of fire
at my ribs, you hid me
from the planes you saw.

I'd stroke your hair
and whisper "It's okay, okay now,"
but you thrashed your legs
and cried as though the covers
might have buried you.
My thighs absorbed the shock,
but never lessened yours.

Once I woke to find you
crawling through the house.
You heard me, leapt, and raised
a carving knife, your blank eyes
seeing someone else
before they rolled back
and you fell toward sleep.

You never woke
remembering the dreams,
but war spilled over,
blood behind your eyes.
"Your words are knives," you said.
"Your wanting bludgeons me to death.
How could you think I'd trust
someone like you?"

You slid your way around
the edges of our rooms,
kept your back from me
against a solid wall.

You saw me cast an eye
toward the door to go,
began to pin me to the bed,
the wall, the floor,
to save your life
instead of mine.

I learned to take
a corner of the bed,
avoid the bruises when I could.
You told me once you feel
so guilty you survived.
I begin to understand.
I finally left a note:
"There is no winning
in this war,"
                                        and left
you crawling through your dreams
so I could sleep in peace.

Kimmika L. H. Williams

NINE YEARS DOWN THE DRAIN

November 29, 1988

Screeching
"You have no home"
while glasses shatter
into jagged splinters
and raw-edged
tears.
Nine years—
count them
nine years down the drain
life's sewage
a murky, muddy,
smelly hodgepodge
of emotions.
Events
frustrations
and dreams.
Nine years
like the fingers on
"his" hand
the littlest pinky
not counting
cut off at the top a bit
that time when
she'd shut it in the door
out of malice.
Nine years
each one
meshing into the other.

Like the runs
in her stockings.
Like the tears
on her face.
Like the steady slur
of obscenities
that they screamed
at each other
while the big picture
mirror
in the living room
caught the reflection
of tussling images
shape
with no shape—
form
that was formed
and then redefined
by the total
nine years
down the drain
along with the wedding band
that she threw
grinding
with the garbage
no less disposable
no more secure
as she screamed,
"You have no home!"
while he
felt for the tip of his finger
that was no more
and believed it.

Donna J. Braswell-Mussato

WHISTLE STOP

for Big Al

The old prizefighter, Al Yeager,
a kid from back of the Chicago stockyards,
his German father beat the hell out of him.
Big Al Yeager in his prizfighting prime
beat up so bad in one New Orleans bout
he had to drink milk from a straw for a week.
He used to come over to watch the Gillette Wednesday night
fights with my father on the old Sears & Roebuck TV.
I'd sit in a corner, listening to the fight
song: *To look right, da da da da da*
To feel right, da da da da da
Gillette Blue Blades: the way to go!

While my father was pulling freight trains
through East Chicago, Hammond, Gary, Indiana,
Big Al kissed my beautiful
red-haired, green-eyed mother.
Didn't think I saw, didn't think I heard him
as he held her, *Nora, you're a fine woman.*
Didn't know she'd been pummeled by
the railroad man—same hand that threw the throttle
on huge diesels, same hand that held
amber bottles at the Fin & Feather.

Reverend Figley had told her, *Go home*
and be a good Christian wife
one afternoon when she'd gone
to Harvey Methodist Church to tell him
the unspeakable things.

After all, who wants to know?
Who wants to hear *You red-headed bitch,*
see his hands reach for her beautiful hair,
clutch it close to the scalp—same hands
that could pick ripe tomatoes without
bruising the skin. *Goddamn drunk,*
kiss my ass right up in the red.
Mother on the kitchen floor.
I have to fight him, she said.

Redwing boot smashing through the panels
of the bathroom door, me and my sister
sitting beside her on the edge of the tub.
The floor is hard, the boot in the back harder.
Outside, train whistles from the Baltimore & Ohio.
(Keep silent. Count your teeth with your tongue.
Push yur cuticles back so hard they bleed.
Do anything, but do not tell.)

Sitting on the front porch,
counting the cars that passed on South Halsted,
I'd watch Big Al pull out of the gravel driveway
in his shiny green Cadillac, Mother beside him.
I knew he could drive her to safety. I always thought
one day he'd come for us in his Cadillac—
he wouldn't fight us, he'd fight for us.
But who wants to come between a man and his wife?

Later, Big Al told me, *Irish, marry*
an educated man. Learn how to bend
like the willow. Don't break like an oak
in a storm.

CHICAGO

Snakes and belly dancers sometimes go together.
I don't mean they date one another
or anything like that,
although I've known quite a few men
who were snakes,
and I don't mean snakes in the grass either,
I mean real pains in the ass,
and the one that comes to mind
is the Greek from Chicago,
as a matter of fact
a lot of pains in the asses—
snakes-in-the-grasses—men were from Chicago
I guess I mean the place of importance
was the place I was born into and grew up out of,
My kind of town, Chicago was, was, was—
people will say,
"And where are you from,"
and
"What do you do,"
and
well, you know how it goes,
so those snakes and those belly dancers
have something in common,
they're related to
(that's right)
men
and I'll tell how that works
or has worked
or perhaps is working right now:
it reminds me of the sleazy dives on South Michigan Ave.
that the men (the real creepy looking men)
ducked into—
I saw them with my own eyes—
they went into those sleazy dives to see
(that's right)
the hootchie kootchie dancers

and those dancers were
(that's right)
women and they had bare bellies and bare
(oh, I hate to even write this)
bare breasts and
(God, I hate to write this even more)
bare bottoms
not bottoms like the song
Bell Bottom Trousers Coat of Navy Blue—
but butts,
bare butts,
and I thought when I was a young girl
riding in my Dad's old Buick
driving past strip joints
in Calumet City on our way to Hammond, Indiana,
why are those women with the bare bodies
on posters in front of those buildings
and one time I remember looking through a partially
open door
(and really saw this with my own eyes)
a beautiful dark-haired woman
was naked,
yes, naked as a jay bird,
dancing on a stage with a snake,
a real live snake,
and I think to myself after all these years
many years,
like this was forty or more years ago,
when I dance and where I dance
I will have all my clothes on
and there will be beautiful music played by an orchestra,
and I will
never dance with a snake in the grass,
I will never
never
dance with a man
who's a pain in the ass.

CAUSE AND EFFECT

"I pass blood . . . sometimes," Juanita confided when they were alone in the kitchen and she was assured by the background humming of the television in the livingroom that she could talk freely.

"Everyone does." Alma smiled, trying to minimize the fear showing in Juantia's eyes. "Even little Marta. I remember she was only a couple of weeks old, we found some blood in her stool. We were scared, took her to the doctor. He just smiled and said, 'In straining she has broken a couple of blood vessels. It's nothing.'"

Juanita didn't say anything. She was just waiting for her to finish, so she could continue.

Alma looked her seventy years—my mother's age if she still lived—dark brown skin, dark eyes, white short, short hair. She preferred it that way. And all those furrows in her face crisscrossing each other. "Do you strain a lot" she asked Juanita.

"Well . . ." Juanita smiled, like continuing a conversation going on inside her head. And smiled again the way people smile to cover up for something and said, "My thing is that I have to be all alone." And her eyes avoided Alma's.

"That's the worst thing you can do. You see . . . When you . . ." Alma was having a hard time finding the words. Defecate, urinate—to elimiate germs. She was searching for the facts from her mental file. "Most of what we eliminate is germs. So when we hold it, germs work their way back into our system."

"I know. I know. But that's my trouble. I need to be all alone. What-you-gonna-do?"

Alma remembered later the pain in Juanita's eyes. And it dawned on her why, why so much pain over something so commonplace, something most people take for granted: going to the bathroom, BM, bowel movements, for Pete's sake! Because Juanita was never alone in the house. With five kids, through the years when one was leaving the other ones were on their way back, since in recent years, three had divorced and come back to live at home. And her grandchildren were there most of the time also. So Juanita was always at someone's beck and call. Especially her husband's. Mario, the Little Tyrant. He is barely 4' 10" of pure selfishness.

Alma could imagine, if nature called while Juanita was serving him breakfast, the way he liked it: *huevos rancheros*, with the homemade chili sauce in the side, the refried beans freshly boiled that morning while he was still in bed. The coffee black and hot, by Jesuschrist, or else! The silverware shining, the napkins from the separate drawer, where the linen napkins were kept, hand embroidered, totally out of keeping with the worn-out linoleum, the rusted stove, the worn-out polished shiny pots hanging on the kitchen walls.

Alma could imagine the discomfort of her having to hold it till the Little Tyrant had finished the *huevos rancheros*, savoring them, soaking their yellow golden juice with the warm, freshly toasted *pan dulce* placed by the side of his plate, lightly buttered. "Watch your hand, not too heavy," he'd tell her. "Sometimes you put too much . . .," he'd say, speaking to her sideways. He didn't need to turn to face her, to look at her. He knew she was there. She wouldn't dare be any place else. Alma could imagine the pain.

Meantime, the Little Tyrant—Juanita had confided—satiated, well, she didn't use that word, full, would push back his chair and go sit on the only toilet in the house. He would have it all to himself, while his clerk opened up the store, placed the OPEN sign in the window. As Juanita talked she giggled at the thought of him in the bathroom at the back of the house, the quietude broken at that time of the day only by the occasional clatter of dishes and pans from the kitchen as she washed and cleaned, preparing to cook his next meal.

For the truth—which infuriated Alma—was, Juanita celebrated everything the Little Tyrant did, or else she covered up for him. As when Alma found her carrying up from the basement an enormous box of heavy dishes for the birthday dinner she was preparing for him. She was out of breath and beads of perspiration had formed on her forehead. "Oh! He would help me if I asked him. Yeah, yeah, he would . . .really," she insisted, seeing the doubtful look in Alma's eyes, knowing she knew he never lifted a finger to help her.

Thirty–five years full of days that succeeded each other just the way he liked them—in quiet and comfort—brought her with a cancerous tumor in her colon to this hospital where Alma found her connected to tubes that sprang from the machine next to her bed. A tube was inserted in her nose, a tube was inserted in her arm, a tube was inserted in her ankle, and a tube was inserted in her bowels from which hung two plastic bags.

Another evening Alma found her with enough energy to hold a conversation. "When you go home, take it easy. Let them fend for themselves. Take care of *you* for a change," she told her.

Juanita looked at the wall, then, holding her eyes on Alma's she said, "I was brought up to serve."

Next visit, Juanita told her, "They are going to discharge me Tuesday."

"In five days? This is Thursday," Alma said, surprised.

"Yes, but I can't go home. Can I stay with you when I come out of the hospital?"

Alma almost choked, but without a pause managed to say, "Of course." Well, her house was going to have to get used to the clutter of a hospital bed, bedpans, walker. She would make Juanita comfortable. Juanita who had mocked her uncluttered livingroom. And gave her opinion of the kitchen furniture: "Ha! Two chairs? What does one do with two chairs? You need to remarry, woman. Have some kids. What does anybody do with only two chairs? Tables need at least eight, ten chairs," and she would laugh, enjoying her own joke while with a critical eye she appraised Alma's business suits and briefcase, mentally placing a price tag on them. A price tag the Little Tyrant would never let her pay. But anyway, Juanita never wore a business suit or carried a briefcase.

"I can't go home to their bickering, their ribbing and shouting at each other all the time. I need quiet and comfort so I can recuperate," Juanita finished.

"Heal."

"Yes."

Alma took mental inventory of the situation, making sure to keep a smile on her lips while Juanita went on confiding in her the truths she had always known although Juanita had never said anything. Because they had been neighbors for all those many years and had become so fond of, really liked, each other. Alma listened and kept her doubts to herself.

Next day she counted the tubes inserted in Juanita. The nose tube had been taken out because the doctor said she was making progress. Careful, getting out what worried her at the moment, Alma asked, "Have you told Mario, does he know you're coming to my house?"

"No. But heck, I'm the one who has to get well!"

Alma smiled and kept her doubts to herself.

Friday night Juanita, still full of tubes, had a new furrow on her forehead. "He's mad because I told him I'm going first to your house, to recuperate." She didn't look directly at Alma. She spoke to the wall.

Alma didn't say anything. She had been hoping her doubts were exaggerated. But she knew that when the Little Tyrant spoke, Juanita did as he bid. For he had his own way of applying pressure. A look, the inflection of his voice, lifting his left eyebrow just so. Not shouting, it was never necessary, just a few decibels would do. Taking off, leaving Juanita to brood by herself.

"Yeah, he's mad. But, like I told him, I need to get well. It's me that's sick."

But Alma knew that if the Little Tyrant got it into his head that Juanita should not see her or talk to her anymore, she wouldn't. She didn't want to lose Juanita. "Your friendship is important to me. I don't want him to get mad at me," she told her.

Saturday night Alma stepped into a room where all she could see were tubes and wires crisscrossing the bed. Wrong room. Checked the number: 117. It was the right room. That was Juanita. "I had a relapse," she whispered.

From that day on, Alma visited her every night. Told her about her day, exaggerating events, making her laugh. Two weeks later the Little Tyrant took Juanita home with him.

Alma went to see Juanita the day after and was shocked to find her sitting in the living room in worn out sweats and sneakers, and to hear that arriving home from the hospital, she had to warm up a can of soup for her own lunch. Alarmed, Alma told her, "You should be in bed."

"Yeah, yeah. What you gonna do?" was Juanita's answer.

Two weeks later Alma found out she was back to cooking in the morning, cooking at noon, cooking in the evening. No one offered to help.

Some days later, early in a bright sunny morning, Alma dropped by to give Juanita a bouquet of flowers from her garden, and found her standing at the sink washing a mountain of pots and pans, silverware, dishes, Pyrex. But over Alma's protests, she served her a cup of coffee and placed the *panera* with freshly baked *pan dulce* in front of her.

Alma stood up. "Let me do it. You're doing too much too soon."

Juanita emphatically repeated her, "Yeah, yeah, what-you-gonna-do?" but rejected Alma's help.

Alma sipped her coffee and peeked into the living room. "Where is Mario?" she asked.

"Oh, he's in the bathroom," Juanita said.

Amudha Rajendran

THE BEATER'S WIFE

This is the only dance I know:
A slip and shimmy taught me once by the
beckoning floor.
A song called gravity, sounding thrush wild
as I hold against this slick stalk I am home to.
I have mimed this ivy-cling,
a spent drop of wax the fire is through chasing.
I have allowed my flesh the shape and proportion
of a wax tear,
shuddering down the candle length.
I have hung by my own weight,
my own body having given me away.
I have been a slight, dissipating thing— smoke,
from a candle just killed.
I have choked my fist into my hot, traitor mouth,
prone to an unseemly wailing noise.
That is why, this stoppage.
I am this accumulation, drawn in haste to the ground,
from so much heat.
You are incarnate, in an astonishing variety of things.
At times, a belt, or flying shoe,
I can find your brand in every slap and sting.
My wet finger calls the direction of this hate
I am your moving target
your bobbing duckling, your treadmill hare,
I am the black sari with blue border, worn over
matching bruises.
I am your black and blue darling,
the quiet thud from your pulsing fist.
I am a fear woman.
I smell the air for hunters.
You told me, in youth, how to sniff the winter—
Since then the chill is all I've known.

I am the frozen buck, obvious in flight
fleeing a predator everyone sees.
Through my selfish nostrils, my breath leaks.
I have tried to kill this seepage. I continue to live.
In my heart, rubies.
Matching those from between my thighs.
I think they are from anger,
which, like my body at dawn, continues to rise.
I am fashioning this blood strand.
The truth for me, an heirloom,
and my heart, an attic.
My heart, full of a preciousness, fragile and rare,
it thrives in that equatorial clime,
little knowing the market has died.

Lanora Cox

A POINTED POEM

I'm so tired of listening to knives,
the chop, chop, chop knife divides
long green onions into little round eyes,
the pace of my job,
legs pumping like knives,
the scissor kick in the air
touching nothing.
At home the knives scratch, seek out the father,
cut out the penis he stabbed into me.
I hear your knives slice the seams of my jeans,
a young nameless amigo proving his macho-ness,
the engraved picture of a doped-up kid
carving my initials into his arm.
They took me away screaming.
The knives of my life reflect
like a hall of mirrors going nowhere.
A marathon of Mac the Knife,
some livelier than others,
some more pointed.

I want to open the drawer and put the knives away,
next to the concave spoons
scoop comfort-food-peace.

I collect spoons to remind me.

Andrea Potos

FIRST BOYFRIEND

I tried to find a reason
for the condom wrapper under his Camaro's front seat,
the morning after he'd gone out with the guys.
I believed him when he said my emotions
were so messy
he had to clean them up
with hard slaps on my cheek. After,
as I slunk down on the cold
porcelain tiles of the bathroom floor,
I was only doing
what I saw a woman do best, my mother—
the bruises budding in her skin
like murky sea flowers,
father's chants of *darling, baby, darling,*
how I watched her rise
as he crumbled and sank, a rubble
of apology at her feet.

Philip Dacey

WHY HE BEAT HER

Because the sun was in the sky.
Because the television hissed at him from a corner.
Because the room was hot.
Because his hands, his hands.
Because his hands detached at the wrists.
Because a fist seeks the resistance of bone.
Because his open right hand and her left cheek
made a most human music.
Because a universe of dust swirling in a shaft of sunlight
accused him.
Because the ringing of the phone startled him.
Because she knew how he felt about the red shirt.
Because he didn't believe her smile.
Because he saw his voice
and flames were shooting out around its edges.
Because he was afraid.
Because her look bore into him and
spun out the other side.
Because her secret kept insulting him.
Because his last word had fallen to the rug
and died.
Because he did not have a gun.
Because the shadow of a tree
lunged through the window.
Because the space between them was intolerable.
Because a bat brushed against
the inside of his skull.
Because her tears dampened the room
to clamminess, and threatened to flood.
Because he wanted to break through to
the silence afterwards.
Because the flowers that blossomed on her skin
invited his kiss.
Because he knew he would beat her in such a way
he would never have to beat her again.
Because a cloud passed in front of the sun.
Because she was holding the ropes of his life.
Because just because.
Because— why else?— he loved her.

Renny Christopher

THERE IS NO BOOT CAMP FOR VIETNAM VETS' WIVES

In my dream
nothing is the same.
I am running,
my feet striking the ground and lifting,
but never fast enough,
never fast enough.
Chasing me is a monster
with the eyes of a man
and the hands of a wolf,
deformed and twisted claws
at the ends of long arms.
When he smiles
yellow fangs break through his beard.
Spanish moss hangs from trees,
reaches out to me in living tendrils
to hold me back,
but I break through, run on,
reach the cliff edge and turn,
my back to the open sky
while my feet dance, wanting to leap over,
but I stay, stay,
and the beast approaches
eyes red in the night.
I open my arms, bare my neck,
stretch out against the night,
and on he comes.

I awake with pounding heart
and shallow breath.
He lies beside me
with the eyes of a man
and the hands of a man,
but still I am afraid,
afraid to move, for fear of
arousing the monster.
In the world of waking,
nothing is the same.

Linda Peavy

THE KILL FLOOR

"It's only because she works on the kill floor they let her juggle her shifts that way. Don't have enough inspectors as it is. Long as she gets the work done, they can't afford to be too tough."

I nod my understanding. Working on the kill floor ought to carry some privilege. I try to imagine this woman I have never seen standing in swirling water, her tennis shoes spattered with the blood of the hogs whose hanging bodies she pokes and prods and stamps with her approval.

"If it hadn't been for her job, she'd have come right home when he first started in on her. But she's put in five years and the minute she leaves, there goes all her insurance."

Again I nod. She'll need insurance. I pour another cup of coffee and try to get the story straight. She's already filed for divorce, but he's changed his mind and says he'll kill her before he lets her go. Last week he broke into the house after she came home from the graveyard shift. And now the sheriff says don't go back home again. She's borrowed a friend's camper and set it up in a campground ten miles from the packing plant. He knows she's going to work every day, and the neighbors say he spends all his time looking for her.

"Isn't she afraid he'll follow her out of the plant? If he sees her getting into her car . . . "

"What car? He's had the car from the first. Left her the pick-up, but the starter's out, so it's parked out at the plant. She's been riding with different ones that live beyond the campground."

"Why doesn't he just follow her when she leaves?"

"That's what I meant about changing shifts. She keeps him guessing as best she can. Oh, she's a sly one. Sometimes she works double shifts, sometimes single. With the truck parked there all the time like it is, he'd have to live in that parking lot to be sure when she's working."

I refrain from telling her that it's just a matter of time before he figures things out. It's obvious that's something she already knows.

"If he ever finds her, she's ready for him." The lines on her face tighten. I do not ask what she means by that.

I do not need to. "She's got a couple of guns and a dog. Just let him try to get into that camper."

Again I try to imagine this young woman I have never seen, strong, even in her fear. Maybe because of her fear. Waiting out her days inside an Apache camper, two guns and a dog to keep her company. "So, what happens if she does shoot him? If she kills him, even?" I have to ask. Have to make her mother see where all of this is leading.

"Then she's done with him."

"With him, maybe. But what happens when the sheriff comes out to see about . . .?"

"Self defense. Everybody knows Ron's nuts. His old man was certifiably crazy. Been in Warm Springs for years. And Ron would have been there too, if it hadn't been for Carla. Time and again I told her to go on and let him go. Manic-depressive, that's what the doctor called it. Sick's all I know. Beating her up like he did last February, dropping out of sight for days, then showing up on Valentine's Day with five dozen long-stemmed roses. Five dozen! It took half her check to pay off Mastercharge."

And the other half to cover the doctor bills. I think it but do not say it. Saying does not seem fair, when we both already know. I look at the woman across from me. She looks sixty, but is probably fifty at most. Once every six months, when the house gets so dirty even I can't stand it, I call Rita to spend a long day helping me clean. A day ahead of her coming, I straighten all the surface debris, shoving things into drawers and over-crowded closets, getting far enough ahead of her so that the assigned task looks possible by the time she arrives.

This morning while she did the bathroom and kitchen floors, I washed windows. This afternoon we'll tackle dusting and vacuuming and maybe shampooing the living room carpet. If we ever get past now.

I did not ask for this. Well, I asked the question I have always asked. How is your daughter? But she has never before really told me. I have never before wanted to know. Nor do I want to know now. I no more want to hear about Carla's being beaten up and raped by her estranged husband than I want to hear how people are really feeling when I ask, How are you?

I do not want to know that this happens to women. I do not want to have this knowledge juxtaposed against my restless chafing in a marriage that has always been viewed as perfect by those who don't live in it. I do not want to have one more reason to see how lucky I am to have such a wonderful husband.

And I do not want to know about something I have to do something about. It is clear that Rita is right. Carla can take care of herself— if it means a shoot-out. But it is equally clear that Carla has no idea how to keep her need to defend herself from this man from turning into a murder rap.

"Look," I say at last. "We can't do anything about this ourselves, but there are people who can. It's the end of October. We've already had snow. She can't stay in that camper all winter."

"She's got a catalytic heater and a down bag. She won't freeze."

I do not bother to talk about what kind of a life this woman will have, there in her camper, snug in the bag, her guns close by her side, fear weighing down on her, keeping her warm through the night. All of that oozes out of the silence and arranges itself in front of us on the table. A proper hostess, I cover the ooze with words.

"But when she's the last camper left, when she's the only one out there, what's to keep him from driving by and getting suspicious?"

"She'll be ready for him."

"But there are other ways." I grope for what they are, for whatever solutions there must be to problems so foreign to my own. "She can go to the Battered Women's Center. They'd have to take her in."

"She's never talked about the place."

"Maybe she doesn't know about it."

"Maybe there's not one down there."

I go to the phone and dial the local center. Surely, there are statewide referrals for such services. The woman on the line is most interested. Too interested. She snatches eagerly at every detail I am willing to give up, right down to how many times he raped her. What if this were my own story I were telling? I would never have gotten beyond describing the way he used the crowbar to break the window on the back door so he could open the deadbolt. I would never have gotten far enough to explain how he didn't put the crowbar down, once he got inside.

Only when I have gone through the litany of abuse, the chronicle of tears and regrets does the woman from the answering service explain that the staff is out. Too spent to be angry for what this woman has done to me and to Rita, who waits at my table, I hang up, armed with another number. All those expensive details have bought me but seven digits to share with the woman who waits.

Her face does not change as I explain that the number is for the county welfare office. There is no center in the place where Rita's daughter waits in her camper for a visit from the man with the crowbar and roses, the man who has no intention of letting her go. There is no home in which she can live without two guns and a dog and the fear.

There is nothing to tell me that Rita has heard what it is that I have so carefully told her. She knew there was nothing that could be done before she sat down at this table. She will know it when she stands up and moves beyond this small, small moment in which we have sat and talked as if what we said might actually matter.

I rinse out the cups, toss the half-eaten sandwiches into the sink, and flip on the disposal. The water gushing out of the tap cushions the blades that slash at the unfinished bits and pieces.

Christina Pacosz

MY MOTHER WITH KOHL ON HER EYES

and an Egyptian smile,
red mouth and hennaed hair.
A brief incarnation
wafting the odor of Juicy Fruit,

face powder and nicotine. This one
is so gay, not like a mother at all.
Such excitement when she arrives home
late in the evening

from the counter at the drugstore.
The Jewish *apoteka,*
where she makes money for Maury and us,
selling Prince Matchabelli,
Evening in Paris, bright lipstick, and eye
shadow which she never wears.
Except in this dream
thirty years later, her eyes weighted
with mystery, her cold eyes
smeared with kohl.
What is she trying to say?
That the dead are beautiful,

living in night dreams
like they never did
in the light of day?
My mother with *al-koh* on her eyes,

made from antimony or galena
for Asiatic eyes,
lidded eyes, black eyes.
Like the one my father

gave her, the one she took
with her when she died. Her flesh
turning yellow and purple
like any common bruise. A single eye,

solitary like the eye of the sun or moon,
the eye of the os weeping blood
each month and my mother
with kohl on her eyes,

what is she trying to say?

Dee DeGeiso

WHAT EVER HAPPENED TO MISS RHEINGOLD?

It was the summer before my mother went crazy, sometime in the early 1950s. Betty and I spent most of our time voting for Miss Rheingold. Whoever won the Miss Rheingold contest would be the national model for Rheingold Beer for the next year. Since Rheingold was a local brewery, the contest was always a hot topic of conversation on the neighborhood porches where everyone gathered after dinner to gossip and wait for the ice cream man. Usually, he turned the corner in his white truck with the loud bell around seven o'clock. Until then, we all talked about the contestants, who were all beautiful and all under twenty, each representing the ideal woman for the older boys on our block whose attention we craved.

In those days, it was safer in the big cities than it is now. At least on the surface. Betty and I, two nervy nine-and-a-half-year-olds, walked into Newark's neighborhood bars without a qualm and asked if we could vote for Miss Rheingold. Sometimes the bartenders gave us huge pads of ballots and we got to vote fifty, maybe a hundred times. Each ballot had six names. Elsewhere in the bar, and outside in the window, were the pictures of the six candidates. I voted for Hillie Merritt because she had beautiful thick brown wavy hair that dipped over her right eye. Her teeth were straight and white, her cheeks were rosy, and she had a dimple just above her upper lip on the right side. She looked the way you were supposed to look if you were really female. Betty voted for somebody named Jolene. Jolene was blond and haughty looking, with a challenging smile and a character line between her eyebrows. Betty liked her light features and her strength, but I preferred Hillie's softer, more princess-like looks.

None of the men in the bars bothered us. Some would smile and ask who we were voting for. Others would ask what grade we were in, and if we knew how to swim. They sat on wooden stools, dressed in short-sleeved shirts and baggy gray or black pants with whiskey glasses or tall bottles of beer in front of them. A lot of them looked tired. Their eyes were watery, and they had red blotches on their cheeks and noses. My mother would have killed me if she knew what I was doing. She didn't think it was safe anywhere around men. Whenever I walked with her she told me never to look inside the bars or taverns, even if the doors were open and I heard laughter and loud music. She said the same thing about barbershops and fire stations, never to look inside them. I figured there was something about men gathered together in one place that spelled danger. I wasn't sure why, but I didn't ask, because I could tell by the tilt of her head and her humming that she didn't want to explain.

I noticed men always looked at my mother. She never looked back, but I knew she had seen them because she would quickly stare in another direction and begin asking me how I was doing, or what I wanted for dinner. She really didn't care about my answer, she just needed a distraction. Her father didn't like men looking at her either. Once, as we were going on some errands she said, "Don't turn around. Grandpa's following us. He thinks he's protecting us." When I asked her what he was protecting us from she just said "other men." I knew she was mad at him when she began walking more quickly, clicking her black patent-leather high heels louder and louder on the sidewalk. I struggled to keep up, finally grabbing on to the strap of her shoulder bag to slow her down.

"What are the other men going to do to us?" I asked.

"Nothing. As long as we're careful."

"What if we're not careful?"

"Always, always be careful. Men are very strong and if you make them mad they can hurt you. It's best to make believe they're not there, the ones on the street. This way, you won't make a mistake. Understand?"

I didn't. But I nodded my understanding anyway, because her voice was getting high-pitched, and she was walking faster and faster and people were starting to stare.

"O.K., good," she said when she saw my nod. Then she giggled and put her arm through mine, and we stopped for cherry cokes at Earl's Sweet Shop. When we came out my grandfather was gone and she took my hand and we skipped down the street together like best friends.

I see now that men always came too close to my mother. Not the ones on the street, or in the bars or barbershops or fire stations. She was careful about them. But the ones we lived with in our small second-story five-room apartment. There were three of them, her husband, her father, and her younger brother. Her husband told everyone how lucky he was because she was a beautiful angel who had deigned to favor him. But he also said he would never allow her to work, even though they needed the money. He had his pride. And I noticed he would never help in the kitchen or around the house, no matter how tired she looked, or how bad her headache was. He was a man after all.

"I'm not going into any kitchen like a sissy," he'd say. "I work all day. Now it's time to be served. Maybe you should take more naps if you're tired instead of playing around all day."

It was obvious that he loved to be seen in public with her. But he was always telling her to push in her breasts, even though there was nowhere for them to go; and he often reminded her to be sure the buttons on her blouse were tightly closed and the zippers on her skirts and dresses were firmly locked.

"Why should some other guy see everything you got?" he'd ask with tight lips. "I don't want you looking cheap, you hear?"

When she was out with him she either looked straight ahead or down at her feet. This way she would never meet another man's eyes, and even inadvertently cause her husband to be suspicious and doubt her fidelity.

"Never look a man in the eye," she told me when I was five and just starting school. "He could get the wrong idea. And remember this, if a man bothers you kick him hard between the legs and run. That'll show him."

When she wanted to learn to drive her husband gave an emphatic "no," which he held to for three years. They argued about it a lot. That is, she asked timidly, he argued. Once her leg was discolored where he kicked her in a rage. Finally, when his sister told him he was being unreasonable, he relented, and taught her himself, complaining and cursing every step of the way. But after she got her license he never let her use the car. Soon she stopped asking. So that was that.

Compared to her husband, her father was quiet, but he watched every move she made. He oversaw her cooking, making sure all ingredients were fresh. He was the one who compiled the grocery lists, selected the butcher, the baker, and the milkman. When we were having fish for dinner he gave her written instructions on how to question the fishman to ensure freshness and flavor. At dinner, he sniffed the food for evidence of butter, which he hated; she swore she never used it. And he would put down his fork and shake his head sadly if the greens were too tough or the meat was over-cooked.

"This is not prepared right," he'd intone. "You didn't pay enough attention." She would lower her eyes and say nothing. But I could see her hands form into fists in her lap.

If she ate too fast, so she could get the next course to the table without delay, he pointed it out, detailing all the digestive upsets that could result. He also preached regularly about the unhealthy effects of drinking any beverage with a meal, usually just as she was raising a glass of iced tea or ginger-ale to her lips. Later, while my mother and I did the dishes and swept the floor, he'd drink his wine, taking long, slow sips as he sat in the over-stuffed easy chair by the living room window, her favorite spot in the house.

"Why don't you tell him to move?" I'd ask when we were done cleaning. "He has his own rocker in his room. That's your chair."

"Sh. Not so loud. No one tells your grandfather what to do. Hey, did I ever tell you the story about the time he threw a whole set of dishes at me because I asked him why he used salt instead of toothpaste to clean his teeth? He nearly knocked my head off with the meat platter. He's quite a character." She laughed. I wasn't sure what was funny.

Most afternoons my grandfather would lie on his bed smoking the strong cigars she hated, as he read the paper or *Time* magazine. Once, without warning, he hung a row of salami and pepperoni from his ceiling. But she didn't complain about the odors that permeated the house. She just opened the windows wide when he was out, and sprayed air freshener into the corners of every room. She was careful.

"It's hard living with your father when you're married," she told me. "You forget you've grown up. So does he."

Her brother said she was a saint. But he wanted to improve her. When he started making a lot of money, a *lot* of money, he didn't move out to make her life easier. He bought her clothes instead. Clothes and perfumes and cosmetics. Lamb's wool and Persian wool, and Chanel No. 5 and My Sin. And she didn't like any of it. She returned it all. And gave him back the money. She wasn't a fancy person. But more importantly, she didn't want her husband to feel inadequate because he couldn't afford to buy her such things. Who knew what he would do if he felt bad?

"Your father is a proud man," she said, when I questioned the wisdom of her returning such beautiful gifts. "When you get married, always make sure your husband feels like he can provide for you. He needs to keep his pride. If you make him feel good, he'll never hurt you."

One night, her brother decided that her hair, which was long, black, and wavy, like Vivien Leigh's, needed styling. So he spread Alberto VO 5, or something like it, all over her head. When he was finished the whole apartment stank like perfumed fat, and her hair was greasy and limp. She whispered to me that she didn't want to hurt his feelings, and admired herself in the mirror he handed her, primping and smiling her thanks. As soon as he went to bed she washed her hair again. Twice. And then she got out the air freshener.

"Don't hurt anyone's feelings, especially when they think they're doing something nice for you," she told me as she combed her hair back into the style she chose. "He means well, but sometimes I wish he'd just leave me alone. I wish everybody would."

"Me too?" I asked, feeling scared.

"No! Not you. You're just like me." Even then, I wasn't sure I liked that.

Her men were too much with her. So she warned me of other men, like the ones who never bothered me in taverns. To her, they were all the same. And she taught me what it would be like when I grew up. She said that a woman must be more than merely submissive. She must be loyal, and share her husband's opinions. To disagree could be demoralizing to him. At the wrong time it could even be dangerous. A woman must lie, must sacrifice anything to enhance her man's ego because "men have to be in charge." That was the way of things. She taught me that a woman's work never ends, and she is often sad.

"The most important thing is to be good in the kitchen," she said solemnly. "A man will forgive most minor weaknesses if he gets a good meal. If you do something wrong and he hits you, be quiet. Cover your head and crouch down. It'll only make him madder if you fight back."

She seemed so sure. I didn't question or contradict her. Now I wish I had. For her own good as much as for my own.

When the men were all out of the house my mother would put on the radio and dance around the living room. She loved the big band sound, especially Glen Miller and Count Basie. But she could dance to anything, even Rosemary Clooney or Frankie Laine. She would kick her legs as high as any Rockette, and spin and spin and spin without getting dizzy. While she moved she giggled like a mischievous child, and tried to sing or hum along with the music. After she was finished, only slightly out of breath, her large, pointy breasts would push her blouse buttons open as she stretched her arms high enough to almost touch the ceiling, then bowed to the floor, sweeping her open palms against the carpet.

In her quieter moments, she would read a newspaper or one of my uncle's library books, especially if it was about economics, accounting, or world history. I can still see her sitting in her favorite chair, with her legs crossed at the ankles and her eyes open wide with hunger as she took in the new information. She told me she always put the books back exactly where she found them, and in the same position. "If they find out I'm reading in the middle of the day, they'll think I'm lazy," she confided.

Sometimes my mother sat outside on the porch waiting for the paperboy to deliver the *Newark Evening News*. That's when some of the neighborhood men on the night shift would stop by and flirt with her. My father never found out. She taught me early never to mention these occurrences to anyone. And since it was the middle of the afternoon all the men we lived with were out of the neighborhood. She didn't want any trouble. Or any company. She just needed some fresh air. Bobby Pope, the cute sailor with the big blue eyes from down the street was particularly persistent. I could hear him from upstairs as he offered her candy bars and boxes of Cracker Jack, and asked her if she wanted to go walking. She was always polite when she refused, and she never flirted back. Men no longer enticed her. They simply wore her out.

Hillie Merritt won the Miss Rheingold contest that year. I was proud that I had such good taste. Soon she was everywhere, on giant billboards, in glossy magazines, even on TV ads. I wanted to be her, glamorous, strong, important. But my mother wouldn't be able to help me. After that summer she got quieter and angrier at the same time. During the day, instead of dancing around the living room she'd lie on the floor with a cold rag on her forehead and cry. When I asked her what was wrong, she'd wave me away with her hand and cry harder, sometimes wailing into the air like a wounded animal, other times punching the floor with both fists, not caring what the downstairs neighbors thought. Her headaches were worse and worse, and she began to get wrinkles around her eyes from squinting with pain. The scariest moments were when she'd laugh without stopping for what seemed like hours at a time. She would clutch herself and rock back and forth, making chilling, inhuman sounds at some private joke. Once she pulled out a whole handful of hair, rolled it up into a ball and put it under the couch. She thought that was particularly funny.

Soon my mother began to hit me. She used the broom handle, the snow shovel, even the wooden serving spoon. Her open hand didn't seem enough. I didn't know why this was happening. I thought I was good. The beatings got harder and harder, and I often had black and blue marks on my legs and hips, and red welts on my shoulders and neck. She came at me when the men were out, no witnesses, and I kept her secret. Our secret. I figured it was a careful thing to do. The men never seemed to notice my wounds, nor her increasingly unusual behavior. I guessed they had more important things to attend to. My mother and I were on our own. We clung to each other, bonded in our secret rage, each blaming the other for our misery, as women were wont to do then.

It wasn't long before I learned that I would never be Hillie Merritt, never be Miss Rheingold. My mother learned that nothing would ever change. She would never be anything more than a servant and reflector for men. It was just too hard for her to fight anyone but me. One day she broke completely, and ran through the neighborhood in her slip screaming about communist infiltrators. She was taken to a sanatorium to rest. I wasn't allowed to visit.

Hillie Merritt went on selling her beer while the neighborhood boys all fantasized about marrying her. My mother's men, my men, went about their business. With the help of my father's sister, I got the meals on the table and kept the house clean, while still finding time to read my library books when nobody was watching. Sometimes I went out on the porch and waited for the paperboy to deliver the *Newark Evening News*. As I sat there alone letting the breeze brush my skin like healing salve, I promised myself that I would never live my mother's life, and I would never again let anybody beat me. How funny that it's the picture of my mother, my abuser, doing her free-spirited dance in our living room and reaching to the sky that helped me keep that promise.

Elizabeth A. Smith

TO MY HUSBAND'S LOVER (1)

he eats slabs of poundcake
braced against the kitchen sink,
cuts thick slices from the middle of the loaf.
the uneaten ends harden,
turn stale, crumble.
collars and cuffs
starched into unbending hardness
leave tight, sharp
creases in his neck:
cotton now becomes stiff,
an armor plated chest.

his evenings are preoccupied.
don't interrupt him at his desk.
his love-making (an oxymoron?)
is a bodily function: elimination.
he may please you,
even satisfy,
but rhythms and desires
must be his own.
(foreplay? isn't that removed
with circumcision?
so what's his excuse?)

all this you may know.

it is easy
at twenty-six
to mistake correction for attention.
you will try to change.
to deflect his criticisms you will
amputate:
hair,
fat,

then toes, even whole limbs.
you will lop off your opinions,
allow him to pulverize
your dreams,
cauterize your
spirit.
battered blue and bruised,
your soul will sneak into the kitchen
on dark winter nights
while he sleeps
oblivious to the cold,
and by the light of the refrigerator,
inventory the pantry shelves
and wonder,
why do you feel so alone?

all this you will learn.

Melissa Capers

THE TENACITY OF VIOLENCE

It would not be exactly true to say that the violence had always been there, in that first relationship. In retrospect, I can create a progression—the arguments increasing in volume, the quick turns away turning into fists against the wall, a thrown glass, an overturned table. But that wasn't violence—we were young, we were broke, we were lesbians in a homophobic town. We were in love, we were angry. All that happened wasn't violence—it was frustration, was passion, was tension, was running out of words.

"You want to know how I feel?" my lover yelled. "This—this is how I feel!"—and then something would shatter against a wall.

But that, that wasn't violence. The violence showed suddenly, and fully formed, and in our bed.

We'd been together nearly a year, been living together more than half of that, sharing her child, a business, a bed. We'd worked together that day, been laughing up the stairs to bed, been giggling, wrestling, nearly naked in the dark, between the sheets. I thought I had caught the mood, thought I had tacit permissions based on this night, the many nights before. I leaned against her, reached between her legs.

She flipped me on my back, put her hands around my neck, and squeezed. I went dead at once—alert and still and watching in the darkness for the red to ease, as she took her hands away.

I lay still in the dark, breathing. "You would have choked me unconscious," I whispered.

There was a rustle, as she fixed the covers on her shoulder. "Damn right."

It was that sudden. That spectacular. A moment, hands against my throat, hands against me, hands apart from me, hands empty of compassion. That was violence. Fully grown and sudden. I had no idea what to do, what it had done to me.

The next day, we got up and went to work and ate and slept and woke up again and again and again and never spoke about that night and it almost faded, like a dream, except for the thrown toaster, the smashed ashtrays—I was flinching at raised voices, I was noticing I hadn't ever thrown a thing.

We lived with a gun. It was a neighborhood of break-ins, stolen cars. Two girls living alone with a baby, my lover's father thought we should keep his .22. "Won't even stop somebody," he said. "So I don't suggest you shoot it. Just hope it scares him away."

At first we joked, casually rocking the thing in our arms on the front porch, letting the grapevine carry the news through the block. If we got scared at night, it did feel better to grip something as we walked downstairs, checked the doors and windows. The little rifle was perfect that way—the stock was small, my hands fit just right around it, my fingers rested comfortably, one on the trigger, the others curled, "sort of like a handshake," on the stock. I could balance the thing in one hand, though two felt steadier as I stepped down the stairs into the dark, the nights that I was scared, alone.

The next time. An argument. One in which I wouldn't cry, wouldn't back down, wouldn't let go. She had taken her daughter, 6 months old, into a crowded dyke bar, had locked her, sleeping, in her carseat, in the owner's office.

I had been there, had seen it happen, had been—paralyzed—in surprise and fear of one more blow-out about decisions about the baby. I had said that I wouldn't stay. She had picked up the kid, taken me home, stuck the kid in bed and come downstairs to settle this.

She kept—defending, explaining, accusing: "What, do you think I'm a bad mother?"

Finally, I said, "Yes."

"I didn't leave her in the car!"

"What the fuck's the difference? What if something—anything—happened? What if she fell? What if there was a fire? What if the cops had raided? You would have lost—"

—I lost the floor. She yelled. And threw a silver ashtray in my direction. Wept. Screamed. Woke the baby. We got her back to sleep. Told me the kid was hers. Told me I didn't know. Told me to mind my fucking business. Told me I was jealous of her friends, no fun, no good at work, a fucking tight-ass.

I told myself I would wait this one out. This was important. The kid was more important than the verdict reached—if she would listen, understand. I told myself I'd ride out the storm, wait my turn.

She came to rest on her back on the floor, finally quiet. It was after 3. I asked if I could explain. She nodded. I spoke in a calm voice, said that she was right—it didn't matter what I thought, but she might want to think about what other folks might think. Social workers. Cops. How would it look to strangers, a baby locked inside an office while her mother parties with the queers?

My lover fell asleep. I don't know when. I got up, walked around, felt the rage course through me—all the waiting, all the flinching, all the time I'd sat and given her her say, her rage, her tears. I wanted her to listen to me, just once. This time, even, when it was about the baby, about my ideas, not about myself, not my goals, my interests, my friends or favorite movie.

And I wanted, at the moment, to walk upstairs and get the gun (unload it), come back down, stand over my lover with the barrel in her face, and wake her up with my foot against her arm. I wanted to frighten her. I wanted her to listen.

I started crying and woke my lover up and she thought I shouldn't be upset—she was tired, it was 4 a.m., goddammit, let's just go to bed.

I decided I was leaving.

In the process of our breaking up, the kitchen table went over a few more times, we lost a few more glasses, she told me she would kill me. I moved in with a woman with an unlisted number, a post office box to hide her address. My lover found the place three weeks later, came crunching up the gravel drive at 3 a.m.

We called the cops. She went away. I moved to another town.

Years went by before my next relationship. I wasn't sure what I'd been waiting for, though I soon saw it hadn't come. In all my time with Trisha, the violence was there.

Trisha was a few months out of a relationship in which she had been thrown through a window, knocked into door frames. Lying in bed with her once, I noticed an indentation on her side, a wide spot between two ribs. It marked where her former lover had kicked her—after a punch had knocked her to the floor.

In the months we were together, Trisha and I discussed the violence that had appeared in our last relationships. We also circled one another, to see which of one of us would bring it to the relationship we shared.

If I raised my voice in disagreement, Trisha flinched. And after watching that too many times, I began to call "time outs," to leave the room when things got out of hand. She followed. She said it was a power-play. She hit me in the back, the arms. I shut my bedroom door. It didn't latch. She kicked it open. I lay in my bed in the dark in old terror and tears. I knew I was stronger than she was. I was two inches taller, 20 pounds heavier. I knew she was counting on me not to retaliate—and at the same time, using my greater size to minimize her actions.

Once, I chased her. I had left an argument, gone into my room (left the door open), begun working at my desk—trying to focus on something new, something that would calm me down. She came in behind me, threw a punch into my ribs. I turned and chased her. Out of my room, down the hall, across the living room. She ran into her bedroom, closed the french doors behind her. I pushed, then went still as I saw her through the window, holding the doors closed. She was terrified.

Once, I threw a glass. She was in her bedroom. I was in the living room. The glass smashed, high, against the wall opposite those french bedroom doors. Despite this, she claims I threw it at her, swears she felt the glass go by her ear.

Once, when Trisha told me what had happened in her previous relationship, she slipped, in conversation, into present. From "she used to..." into "she kicks me, she blows her top, the smallest thing will set her off..." Trisha was still talking about her former lover, used her former lover's name. But even so, I stilled in my chair, looked down, felt my face go white. She probably did hear the glass go by.

I had a dream once, in that time after fleeing that first lover, and before I'd ever met Trisha. I dreamed we were in bed again—me and that first lover. I was on top of her. I had a knife against her throat. I wanted her to listen. Just like that night I wanted to use my words—and then that gun—I wanted her to listen. My voice and hand shook as I pushed for her attention. And in a silent, sudden moment, the knife slipped in.

I was drenched with her blood—and she was dead. I stood up the darkened bedroom, shaking, trying to decide what next to do. I woke up, drenched with sweat, and took a silent shower, and tried to figure out what all of this had made me.

John Sokol

SESTINA FOR PARTING JAGGED

We could have made another house of cards. What remained
after all the wretched, heart-breaking pains
was something-barely-possible and a lot of odd pieces
that once we matched when we were tuned finest,
when the bourbon was neat and the night was jagged,
like our serrated parting, and now the silence strange.

They say people don't change. But isn't it strange,
they always think they do? All along, you remained,
I remained, much the same, and therefore parting jagged,
found our ways, each to mollify our private pains
and still maintain a stance of purpose. Our finest
hour: each not knowing the other's heart was torn to pieces.

But no more tongue-in-cheek and my speaking of your pains
because what I need now is that bourbon jagged
and the night neat in a cocoon of numbness. Pieces
of my heart hang before me like a carrot. Strange
distortions of how things were confound my finest
dreams of how I wish they had remained.

Ours—a history of endless weird riddles. How many pieces
does it take to make a whole? Which scenes are too strange
for the proud memory's remembering? Why are ineffable pains
attached to common objects? Which of us remained
most callous to the bone-blade of these jagged
conundrums? Solving these would have made farewell finest.

But I remember the night it all went jagged,
when anger—foolish and tangible—scattered the pieces
of reason we had piled together between us. What remained
was what only bourbon could for a while subdue. The finest
blend would be the one that numbs our partings strange
and renders our life together devoid of all its pains.

To turn back time and keep of ourselves what's only finest
involves a wish that merely underlines the pains
of not having done so then. It's too late and too strange
to think of smoothing all the stones of all the edges jagged,
for what remains still is all that then remained
when the house fell down and we were among its pieces.

Only a lesson has remained. When we aren't at our finest,
we could be worse. When nights are strange let's take the pains
to gather scattered pieces, otherwise the parting's jagged.

Paul Truttman

TERMINATION

She wants affection,
he wants another drink.
She wants to go out,
he wants dinner in.
She wants pretty things,
he wants the plain.
One wants to romp;
should be two as one.

They sit in silence,
having again fought.
He in anger, she in tears.
They live together, forgetting
they were once in love.

Problems escalate
building full force.
They question not their rights,
simply deny every one.
Without each other, love turns sour,
termination imminent, a total loss.

ASHES IN AN URN

We cannot apologize or even ask for their forgiveness for we know not where they are. We cannot tell them that if knowing what we know now, their early demise would not have happened. We cannot tell them that we had alternatives, that their death was a mistake. We cannot tell them that we would reverse time if we could. My wife, a victim of spousal assault and murder— resides in an urn.

There is perhaps only one thing worse than taking another's life (except in self-defense or war), that is not accepting responsibility for the act— and allowing the victim's early demise to pass without meaning. I would like my wife's death to have some meaning! There is no appeal. And the action cannot be rationalized— nor should it be. Both mind and soul were weak.

The killer (or abuser) is usually weak-minded, unable to deal with the pressures of a given moment, and causing others immeasurable grief. Beware! There are those among you who are just as weak.

Katharyn Howd Machan

BATTERED

Not the women's Community Building, that's
the obvious place. Paper bag of clothes,
toothbrush, comb, somehow a small china cat
grabbed and stuffed in a pocket. Run,

no, walk quickly to the corner, turn
and hope the darkness falls behind you
like a lead curtain, heavy,
the bib at the dentist's office.

Money, how much money? Call—whom?
Can't try the police, they'll say
get-back-where-you-belong. Air
cold, red sneakers on the sidewalk,

scrambled eggs for supper hard in your gut.
He'll tear the place apart, break dishes,
he'll be drunk. You walk fast.
The wedding album flashes to your mind,
two strangers surprised in white and black.
Who might see you hesitate, chest sore
where he kicked? Which bar is he
laughing in, how long before he returns?

You'll not return, never, you'll find a room,
a warm place, a new name.
Enough, you say, enough. As long
as no one knows, no one must know

how love has come to this.

Kennette Harrison Wilkes

HE SHARPENS HIS WIFE'S BONES

He cuts cheap linoleum for her kitchen.
He cuts peach and plum and pear limbs
  to play God with grafts.
He cuts wild root stock
  heart hymen oozing blood sap.
He cuts the cloned fruit from alien limbs
  hybrid excellence weighing down
  the raped virgin.

He cuts Thanksgiving turkey
  its legs still wired together
  skin, shine tight, near to burst;
  stuffing swollen like a giant infant trapped.

He cuts paths through the woods
  criss-cross like the top
  of the Christmas ham;
  the deer on the other side
  of the pineapple-ring sight
  stands still, its cherry heart
  lined up in the cross hair.

He cuts the thread he loops around
  his son's loose tooth.
  You don't want to swallow it, do you?
  You want the tooth fairy to come, don't you?
  Big smile, now—big smile.

He cuts the cork from another wine bottle
  with the knife his grandfather gave him.
He cuts the strap from his daughter's slip
  in his dreams.
He sharpens his knife. He sharpens his knife
  on his wife's bones.

He sharpens the knife that cuts the line
  they never cross down the center of their bed.

Martha Clark Cummings

THE DUTCHESS

I go around the corner to The Dutchess about three times a week. Who am I kidding? Exactly three times a week. On Sundays after ten. On Wednesdays and Thursdays I walk up from my lousy job as the only "administrative assistant" to these three jokers who sell surplus parts on Canal Street and go right in and have a few beers without even going home first.

I don't go near the place on Friday and Saturday nights when the kids from Queer Nation take over. It's too depressing. I'm too old. Who needs it? On Fridays and Saturdays I rent a video or two, buy myself a six pack and a couple slices of pizza, and try to learn how to be my own best friend. By Sunday evening I've had it with keeping myself company and am back at the bar again.

Before we broke up, my ex, Monica, explained that you have to be really good-looking (like she is. She didn't say this but it was implied) to meet someone in a bar. Either that or you had to have terrific breasts. Otherwise, who would notice you? Why would anyone even see you through the smoke, through the thick crowd of women's bodies. Why would anyone squeeze her way through the crowd to ask you to dance if it didn't seem worth it? No reason at all. That's what Monica was telling me I've got to offer. Absolutely nothing that would make another woman slide down off her barstool and come over to ask me to dance. I have to do all the sliding and walking and asking. I'm aware of that. I know what my options are. Do the walking or don't get any.

Lately, since Monica and I broke up, I haven't been doing much but looking and trying to stay out of trouble. It doesn't mean I don't go to the bar, but I don't ask anyone to dance much. I'm waiting until I'm sure I can trust myself again. After what happened with Monica, I don't want to rush into anything new.

Last week, though, I started chatting with a small squat woman with very short red hair— she was almost bald-looking. She was sitting on the stool next to mine and I was looking at her severe hairdo thinking that my own hair could use a trim, that I'm starting to grow little wings out of the sides of my head. When I'm not trying to pick a woman up I have no trouble at all starting a conversation. I had ordered a Bud Lite and settled in for another evening of getting my clothes stunk up with cigarette smoke and stained with the drinks women were going to spill on me as they tried to squeeze between me and the woman next to me to order, when the bald-headed woman, whose name was Lucy, and I just sort of struck up a conversation. I wished I could have taken out a piece of paper and written the beginning down for later when I'm trying to pick up one of the pretty ones and am all tongue-tied. Anyway, I was thinking so hard, trying to replay the conversation in my mind, "What'd she say?" "What'd I say?" that it wasn't until old Lucy laid her freckled hand on my arm and said she was sure she had seen me somewhere before that I realized *she* was trying to pick *me* up. Right away I started to feel that familiar ache between my thighs. This embarrasses me a little.

Lucy asked me if I wanted to dance—just get up and shuffle around a little, was how she put it. It was a fast song. I thought that was sort of cute and decided to cut myself a little slack. With Lucy, dancing didn't seem dangerous. She wasn't one of those types I have to watch out for. She was dressed in an old flannel shirt and had a really sad expression in her eyes, like she had had more than her fair share of hard times with women, too. I was telling myself that maybe we could just go back to the tiny dance floor where several couples were already jostling each other like billiard balls and the smoke was hanging like fog from the ceiling, the star-making machine was twirling, that Lucy and I could just grind it up a little on the dance floor, no harm done, a little kissing, maybe, a stray hand sliding down her thigh...But then I caught sight of her butt. Lucy looked like she had a pantload of cottage cheese. Too bad because her face was pretty, but I sat right down on my stool again and said thank you I was comfortable where I was. Monica used to say that with looks like mine I had no right to be so fussy. I told her that as long as I could get what I wanted, I was going to go on being as fussy as I damn well pleased.

After I turned her down, Lucy's shoulders tensed and her hands bunched up but then she took a deep breath and started chatting again, as if it were no big deal. This is what I need to learn how to do.

On Thursdays, I get there early, sometimes around 5:30 or so, and watch the place fill up with women. It's like being the first one at the beach and then getting surrounded by bodies. Before you know it, there are women everywhere you look. Lately they seem to have a new position they like. This sounds like I'm talking about sex but I'm not. What happens is that one woman sits on a stool with her back against the bar and her partner or whatever you want to call her (I prefer girlfriend) backs up to her and then the one on the stool wraps herself around her, arms and legs. Like any minute the one standing up is going to take off with her girlfriend on her back, piggy-back style. To them this seems romantic. Who am I to judge?

A woman with thick dark hair down to her waist, hair that makes her hold her head very still and get a sort of arrogant look on her face, has squeezed between me and the woman on the next stool three times already. I could reach right out and pat her butt if I wanted to. It's cute enough. I don't do that sort of thing. Also, I have the feeling that she would put up with it in a way that would be insulting to me. What I mean is, she would smile indulgently, thinking of me as harmless, the way nurses treat little old men in wheelchairs who grab at them.

Each time the girl squeezes in—she's wearing a tight black sweater and black jeans and cut off cowboy boots, a totally familiar outfit—Lee, the barmaid, rushes right over to serve her, dropping everything. Lee and I used to have the kind of relationship that consisted of rolling our eyes at each other when somebody got loud and giving each other knowing looks when somebody was putting on the make. She is also likely to yell out, "Keep it clean, girls! This is a family bar!" She is from the Midwest and when she does this, it's convincing, and for a moment there's an awful hush that comes over the place. The women look at each other, bewildered, like they're asking each other, "How did somebody's mother get in here?" Then everybody starts laughing when they realize it's just Lee.

Right after she heard about what happened between me and Monica, Lee started keeping away from my end of the bar unless I called her over to order another beer. She brings me my beer and I am grateful for that, since there's a sign hanging over the bar that says, "We reserve the right to refuse to serve anyone for any reason." But she won't talk to me or even look at me anymore.

"What can I get you, sweetheart?" Lee asks the girl.

"My name is Chloe," says the girl with long hair in a snotty tone, "and I'd like a Rusty Nail."

"Coming right up," Lee says, nonplused. She's the kind of person you wish you'd had for a best friend in high school. She would have calmed you down when you were itching for a brawl.

This Chloe is just a kid. They probably checked her ID at the door. A kid with long shiny hair which she pats and fluffs like she brought her Persian cat along to the bar with her. This hair of hers sets off red flashing lights in my head, like being pulled over by a state trooper. Monica, too, spent too much time and energy fussing over her hair, which was thick and wild and auburn, the way you'd expect someone with her name's hair to be. She would be looking in the mirror, fixing it, fussing, fussing, fussing with her hair, tying it up, letting it down, fluffing it...oh so preoccupied, while I'd be standing behind her, the cords in my neck bulging, shouting about how she was torturing me, making me feel like an animal. She did not even turn around. She looked at my image beside hers in the mirror and talked to *that*, as if *that* were doing the yelling. I tried to restrain myself. I really did. This went on for a long time before I finally broke down and let her have it.

Chloe is standing right next to me. I can feel her hip bone pressing against my waist. She is going to keep standing there, her skinny body pressed against the bar, watching Lee work. It doesn't matter since I am definitely not interested in her at all and I have to go pee.

"Sit down for a minute if you want," I tell her. "I have to go downstairs."

"Thanks," she says, unnecessarily grateful.

When I come back upstairs, Chloe is perched, tentative as a sparrow, on my stool. She watches eagerly as I squeeze through the groups of hefty women gathered near the bar.

"Do you want to dance?" she asks before I get to say a word.

She is tall and very thin. The kind of girl who spends her whole life dreaming of being a model, the kind of thin, frail, pretty girl you could pick up and toss into your bed. Her hands are long and slender and her bony knees protrude through her tight jeans. I could hold both of her wrists in one hand.

She is waiting for an answer. I nod.

On the dance floor she is reserved at first. I try to pull her closer and she resists a little, as if she were saying "Maybe." Not, *no*, exactly, but *maybe*. Her skinny body, her ribs and shoulder blades feel tense, uncertain, like she's not sure she's safe. Then a fast song comes on. We dance and dance and dance.

By ten o'clock our bodies are soaked with sweat. Chloe shyly takes my hand and slips it up under her sweater and onto her bare back to show me how wet it is. Meanwhile the strobe light flashes and the room seems to whirl and the other couples keep right on dancing. We start up again and before long it's like we are all tumbling around together in a giant cocktail mixer and I am not even thinking. I have switched from beer to straight scotch to beer again. Lee keeps serving me the drinks. I don't even look up when I hand her the money. I watch the dollars go from my hand to hers and that's it. I know that if I looked up at her, she would give me a look that said, "I'm watching you," or "I'm thinking about warning your new girlfriend," so I keep my eyes down.

At midnight the songs on the jukebox get slow. This is a kind of tradition at the Dutchess. After midnight on week nights we all start to slow down and face the fact that we have to go back to work the next morning. Chloe takes off her sweater and doesn't hold her body away from mine anymore. Her breasts are round and firm and press against mine in a way that makes me want to lift her thin cotton undershirt right up and put my mouth on them. As we sway to the music I take hold of her waist and pull her close and begin, very slowly, to move my hands. I can feel her ribs under my fingers, and I start sliding my hands forward, and she is not saying no. She is letting me put my hand up onto her breast, right there on the dance floor. I push my face into her neck and smell her sweet flesh and want much more of her. I am so surprised by her willingness that I can hardly remember what to do. By the time it comes back to me her hand shoots up and drags mine back down to her waist and she whispers, "Not here." And in spite of all my promises to myself, I whisper back, "Where, then?"

She pushes me away from her, gently, almost as if she pities me for how much I want her, how easy it's going to be to bring me to my knees.

"I'm not ready for that yet," she says with a sweet smile. "Could we just dance for now?"

"Okay," I tell her, trying to seem cool and composed although my breath is coming out in gasps. "No problem."

I pull her back to me and we dance and I don't try anything again.

"Be grateful," I instruct myself, "that she doesn't want to move in tonight and begin a long term monogamous relationship."

Lee is yelling "last call." I go back to my stool and sit down. Tomorrow at work I am going to feel like hell. Suddenly it doesn't seem worth it.

"Let's sit this one out," I tell her.

"But it's the last song," she says, pleading. "They're going to unplug the jukebox." She seems like she might start to cry.

"I'm tired," I tell her. "I need a rest."

I order my scotch and beer at the same time. She sits down beside me, brooding. She tosses her hair over her shoulders angrily now, as if it were a package she was tired of carrying. Then she gets up. We say goodnight. No phone numbers. No "Are you sure you wouldn't like to come over?" Then, on Friday morning, in the middle of typing a dumbass memo, my head pounding, I start feeling like a damn fool. What if she never comes back? What if I never see her again? She was vain and all but for God's sake we were practically doing it on the dance floor and I didn't even get her phone number.

There is no way I'm going to wait until Sunday, either. Friday night or not, at 8PM, before they start charging a cover, I'm back in The Dutchess again, pretending not to be looking for her.

When she comes in she walks right up to me, like she knew I would be there. She tosses her long hair over her shoulders and says, "Let's dance," like she owns me or something. She has a dark green silk blouse on. I see that her nipples are hard and I slide right down off my barstool and out onto the dance floor.

This time, though, I am the one who holds back when the slow songs start. I am the one who waits, who resists, who says, "Maybe." Chloe holds me tighter, pulls me closer, her strong lean thighs parting over one of mine, her body swooping down to rub against the coarse fabric of my jeans.

Then images of the last time with Monica start filling up my mind. I try to push them away but they won't let me. I keep seeing it, again and again, Monica's shocked expression, the glass shattering, the way she tried to protect her face by holding up her forearms, her bleeding forearms, the floor slick with beer, my knees soaked with beer from when I slipped, the handful of her hair that I found in my pocket, much later, when I was out walking, out praying she would have the sense to pack up and get out before I came home again.

"Can I walk you home?" Chloe asks.

I am tempted to say no. I am strong enough to refuse her now and it would be just what she needed to keep her interested. But I am trying to be good. I am trying to behave like a normal person. I tell her okay, I would like that.

We stand in the raw cold on the steep red steps in front of my apartment building, leaning against the shaky wrought iron railing. She is huddled up in her coat and would probably like to be invited in.

"Well, thanks," I tell her. I give her my most generous smile and touch her cheek with one finger. "See you."

"Tomorrow?" she says, stepping from one foot to the other, like a child. "Will you be there tomorrow?"

I feel a different kind of smile spreading across my face.

"Maybe," I tell her. "Maybe not."

"It's Saturday night. You must know if you're busy or not," she says, smiling. She likes this game.

"I do. I just don't know if it'll be worth it or not for me to go into that smelly old bar again."

"It *will* be worth it," she says.

"Okay," I tell her. "Then I'll be there." And I turn and go up the stairs.

On Saturday I feel uneasy all day. I don't have the office to distract me. I don't have my three creepy bosses and their surplus supplies to get angry at. I cannot stop thinking about Chloe. I cannot. I try to go back to sleep, to read, to listen to the radio, to go for a walk, even watch a little daytime TV, but all I am doing is waiting for it to be night. I pace the floor of my apartment and watch the sky turn dark. I make myself some supper so I won't get drunk too fast. I even stand in front of my closet and worry about what I'm going to wear.

It is almost ten o'clock when she arrives. I have had two scotches and several beers already, served by Lee, who gloats because I am there and I am alone. Chloe's face brightens when she sees me. All innocence.

"You're here!" she says, as if she's surprised. As if she did not make this whole thing happen. She checks her coat because it's very crowded with girls in spiky hairdos and leather and black tube skirts and little black shoes. She squeezes between me and the woman on the stool next to mine. I have on *my* silk blouse tonight. She is wearing a sweatshirt.

"You look beautiful," she says, then kisses me, for the first time, pressing her soft mouth onto mine.

"Let's dance," she says.

At four o'clock in the morning, when the bar closes, I am drunk and very steamed up. I invite her upstairs. What choice do I have? She sits down at the kitchen table and looks around but says nothing. There is nothing to say. It is not a nice apartment and I have done nothing to make it nice. What was nice, Monica took with her.

I ask her if she wants another beer. She says yes although her head must be spinning too. As I hand her the glass and bottle, the stuff with Monica looms up again. I push the images away. I close my eyes for a second. The room spins. Meanwhile, Chloe pours herself a glass of beer and moves over to the sofa. I can hear her doing this.

When I open my eyes she pats the place beside her. I don't even remember sitting down but then we are kissing, my tongue inside her mouth, and I am pushing her onto her back, not roughly but like I mean it, getting on top of her, prying her legs apart with one of mine. I kiss her neck, her throat, my mouth moving down toward her breasts. She is moaning a little, moving under me like she wants more. I start kissing her breast right through her undershirt, getting it drenched. I am lost now, completely. There is no going back from this. I reach down and unzip her jeans. With my other hand I take hold of one of her wrists, then the other one, and hold them, tight, over her head.

I was just going to slide my hand into her jeans and rest it there. I wasn't going to do anything. I was going to wait until she started to move, until she showed me what she wanted. But she must have gotten scared or something.

Because suddenly she yanks herself away from me, pushes me off of her, then sits up, wild-eyed.

"What's going on?" she says.

I can hardly breathe. I can hardly believe what's going on inside my pants. It flashes through my mind that I could grab her hand and put it there and say, "This. This is what's going on."

I don't say anything. I sit very still and wait.

"I'm sorry," she says. "I haven't made love with a woman in a really long time." She gives me what she must think is a significant look. "I guess I'm not quite ready yet."

She gives my hand a little squeeze, then drinks down her beer. She stands and zips her pants. She goes into the kitchen, setting the empty glass on the table. I wait.

"I guess I should go now," she says.

I might have been all right. I might have been able to let her put on her coat and walk out the door.

But that isn't what she does. She stands in the middle of the kitchen, under the light, takes a mirror out of her bag and starts fixing her hair and checking her eye makeup. When she sees me coming toward her, she smiles.

Lenore Baeli Wang

BATTERED WOMAN'S ALPHABET

Inside A a woman squats in the Attic,
her Breasts squeezed tight into their cups
Constricting the breadth of them,
praying the Door will keep her sealed
away, her husband thinks the attic Empty—
Fear not yet enabling her to fly.
Caught inside the Gullet
Half out half in,
if only she could climb right out on top,
Jump off
Kick out
sit straight upon a Lap of love;
a Mouth keeps snapping,
then her heart slides dowN.
Inside an O it feels a perfect fit;
she rises to the toP, then
slides right down the tail inside the Q;
she Runs as if a P's become an R,
Slipping
through Time's openings
with open-mouthed Understanding
Victory brings,
Wins,
signs her own mouth with a kiss
Yells
and iZ gone.

Emily Robertson

NOBODY EVER ASKED

but i will tell you anyways
  how i got out of the situation
i called my daddy and told him
things had really gotten out of
hand
the front door had been kicked in
i had to flush somebody's vomit down the toilet
i wondered who'd been loved in my bed
'cause it wasn't me
see
i'd spent the night at a
girl friend's
put on my nylons without
forcing a run and faked my way
through another day
at the beauty salon
to come
home to this
so my daddy said put him on the phone
dad
must of said something mighty
must of said something mean
'cause all my
troubles in the world
the boy
the man
sat down in his favorite chair
the one he always sat it
the beige upholstered one that spun
round so in better days he could watch tv
in the living room or me in the kitchen
without moving from his favorite corner
anyways

he sat down and cried
he said I was a traitor
that i sold out to the white man
   something down and out black men
tend to say to deep black women that just
wanna get up and out the situation
i watched his tears
hungry crocodile babies
crawl one by one down his hollow cheekbones
i wondered briefly were they manufactured
or real liquid anguish
soon discovered that i did
not care
later his mom and sister
came to pick up his television set
talkin' through southern tongue clicks
the mother says
i wish it hadn't come to this
me
i couldn't wait to close the remains of
that splintered door behind them

ABUSIVE MEN

spoiled boys make dangerous men
neglected boys make dangerous men
having no power makes dangerous men
too much power makes dangerous men
someone tell him/'cause he does not know/
it was not her,
the one that said love me/love me/
but could not wait any longer after
five years in the marriage
tell him
it was not her fault
don't blame her
or
did she hold a gun to your head
and beg
hit me
blacken my eye
ask him/try and remember/
did she ever say
beat me
that is how I want to die?
he says
she drove me to it
he says we couldn't understand
because we never knew her/
ask him
why didn't you just walk away?
or did she hold a gun to your head
and force you to stay?
tell him we never knew her
but we know she didn't want to die
that way

Leilani Wright

BLOOD WORDS

You have heard the saying about words—
how they're not only cheap,
they'll give themselves away?
That is not entirely true.
Words have cost me plenty once or twice,
like when I tore my partner
limb from bloody limb with them.

The savaging had to pass.
And when the color red faded from my eyes,
I found it puddled on the floor
and streaked across the bedroom mirror.
Obscenities were fingerpainted on the walls.
Features hung from the ceiling fan;
an appendage leaned in the corner
with the finger pointed toward me;
an enormous tongue lay neatly centered
on an antique coffee tray
like a table sculpture
passing for disturbing art.

I can take out a loan to cover all the surgery,
choose each word carefully from now on,
pay cash up front.
But the contract puts a lien
on our relations,
and the debt is what binds us.

Sue Doro

RUTHIE

she sure could laugh

one time we were practicing basketball
after school
in the old Saint Thomas Aquinas gym
on Milwaukee's north side
her and Mary Ellen and I
when Ruthie slipped and
tripped on her own foot

she started to laugh
sitting on the floor where she fell
laughing and holding the basketball
against her belly
laughing so hard
tears were dripping from her eyes

Mary Ellen and I were laughing too
just watching Ruthie laugh
when a little river of something wet
began to grow under Ruthie

it trickled and weaved its way
across the old wooden floor
like a grass snake
and three twelve-year-old girls
eyed it giggling and gasping for air
on the basketball court
three twelve-year-olds
in the autumn of 1949
just a wall and a flight of stairs away
from the church sanctuary

Ruthie
she sure could laugh

Ruthie's Ma ran a sewing machine
in a clothing factory

she had a few years to go
before retirement and talked about
when she'd have more time
to sew anything she wanted
instead of pants zippers
over and over again

she'd sit in a big stuffed chair
in her front room on Saturday mornings
and crochet doll clothes for Ruthie and me
she'd hold up a little hat or a coat
for us to see and she'd talk about her job
she said she didn't mind working at the factory
she liked the women she worked with
and sometimes when the nice foreman
was on their shift he'd let them speak
to each other while they worked

she kept on crocheting while she talked
and when she finished a tiny scarf
or a pair of doll mittens
she'd give them to us right away
and then get up and go in the kitchen to bake
she smelled of cinnamon and hot coffee
and made apple pancakes for us to eat
while we dressed our dolls

some Saturdays I'd call for Ruthie
with my brother's coaster wagon and we'd travel
up her alley to the drinking glass factory
by the railroad tracks

the people made frosted glasses
with painted flowers on the sides
and we knew when they threw away the rejects
so Ruthie and I would try to be there
to rescue the best for our mothers

sometimes we'd find big sheets of cardboard
behind the factory and use them to slide downhill
on our fannies to the tracks in the gully
once we took turns riding down

on an old rocking chair
'til it broke into pieces

we'd listen for the trains before we slid
and watch and wave at the engineer when
one went by
he'd smile and wave back
and Ruthie would laugh and so would I

Ruthie
she sure could laugh

on cold days
Ruthie would play the accordion
for her Ma and me
when Ruthie played
her big dark eyes would light up
her cheeks would get pinker
and her black hair would curl closer
around her face

once when we were playing
her Ma told me she looked like her father
Ruthie's dad was killed in a foundry accident
when she was still a baby
her Ma had his picture
on a shelf in the dining room
behind a dried braided palm branch
and a white candle
tied with a purple ribbon

one time I told Ruthie she was lucky
at least there's no yelling and arguing
if her father was dead

"Ruthie," I said, "you're lucky."
and she answered, "I don't know."

Ruthie was a good Catholic girl
said a rosary every day
and got married
at sixteen

birthing five baby girls
five kids in five years
one right after the other
all dark hair dark eyes
and pink fat cheeks

she'd wanted to finish high school
but that didn't work out
Ruthie started with the rest of us
from Saint Thomas
at Cathedral High
downtown on Wells Street

it cost money to go to Catholic
instead of public high school
and I remember my father complaining
about the tuition and my mother arguing
that it was a sin not to send me there
anyway I guess they managed
because my father was a welder
at A.O. Smith's

but Ruthie's Ma didn't have enough money
for tuition from her job
so she went to see Monsignor Shanahan
at Saint Thomas
and he told her to never mind
he'd take care of it
after all it was a SIN
not to send your children to a Catholic school

Ruthie's mother didn't want to sin
so she sent her daughter to Saint John's Cathedral
and when it came time to pay the semester bill

she went to the church rectory
but the Monsignor just couldn't seem to recall
ever talking to her the first time

Ruthie's Ma didn't have the cash
she couldn't pay the bill
so sin or no sin

Ruthie was asked to leave Saint John's

her mother enrolled her at Washington High
on Sherman Boulevard but she was lonely
she didn't know anybody
she ended up getting pregnant
by the boy across the street
from the drinking glass factory
had to quit school at sixteen
and get married
producing five baby girls
one right after the other
five kids in five years
Ruthie was a good Catholic girl

after the wedding
Ruthie had to move to the south side
her husband quit school too
and the only job he could find
was at a gas station in Caledonia

Ruthie missed her old neighborhood
and every chance she could
she'd make the bus trip
across the Twenty-seventh Street viaduct
to visit her Ma on Thirty-second Street

she'd always bring the babies along
her Ma said she loved it
she crocheted baby clothes
and fed them homemade applesauce and cookies
while Ruthie played her accordion

I was a few years behind Ruthie
in marriage and babies
when she was pregnant the fifth time
it was my third
my husband was gone a lot
he said the kids made him nervous
his job made him tense
he needed time alone he said

anyway Ruthie and I would be on the phone
every day talking babies and husbands and
never having enough money for anything

when I was depressed
she could always cheer me up
with stories of funny things her kids did

sometimes I babysat for Ruthie's kids at my place
but I never brought mine over to her house
because of her husband

Ruthie said he wasn't a bad man
and he was happy when he fixed cars
but he'd hit her when he got drunk
and if the babies got in the way
they'd get slapped around too
once Ruthie called the police
but they told her
there was nothing they could do
it was her problem

Ruthie told me I was lucky
my husband didn't hit me when he got mad
he'd just stay away from home longer

"Suzie," she said, "you're lucky."
and I answered, "I don't know."

Ruthie jumped off her garage roof
in the eighth month of her last pregnancy
she phoned to tell me and when I asked
if she was o.k. she answered
"Yeah, nothing happened."
and then she laughed

and one Saturday morning about a year later
she took the five little pink-cheeked girls
to her mother's house and left them there
eating apple pancakes

and never returned

her mother called to ask me
if I knew where Ruthie was
that's how I found out that she was gone

I never heard from her
back then or since
I only know that
Ruthie survived the only way she could
and protected her children
by giving them away

I also know that I miss her

but the Ruthie I remember
was my girl friend when I was growing up
I can see her face
as she plays her accordion
I hear her squeals of delight
as she slides downhill to the railroad tracks
I think of Mary Ellen, Ruthie and me
playing basketball
in the old Saint Tom's gymnasium
and I can still see Ruthie
sitting on the floor in a puddle of pee
laughing and holding the basketball
against her belly

Ruthie
she sure could laugh

Brenda Shaw

LUCKY

Sometimes
when I play with the ensemble
we do Brandenberg 5—
you remember? It has that
lovely lyric in the last movement.
We wrote a little love song for it
and used to sing it
when we played the record.

Now I play the *ripieno* part:
one steady note per measure
while the flute
takes the melody.

I wonder—if there *is* telepathy
maybe you're hearing us play it,
wherever you are,
and saying "She does remember;
yes, she *does* remember,"
and for a moment I wish
you'd walk through that door
and tell me that you've heard.

But then I recall the fear,
and how it was before I ran away.
You said you'd kill me
if I tried to leave.

Last night I saw a documentary
about the woman
who did everything right,
availed herself
of every legal move to protect her
from her violent husband.

"If you leave,
I'll find and kill you,"
he told her.
And he did.

The police, the magistrate,
the judge, the district attorney
couldn't stop him—
or rather wouldn't.
Wouldn't apply the law.
Wouldn't charge him with
the battery, the assault,
the kidnapping.
Turned him loose after eight hours.

Three weeks later
he killed her,
shot her down
in front of their children.

He was convicted of First Degree Murder.
At sentencing the judge apologized:
"Sorry I had to do this, but under the law
it's the only thing I could do.
Best of luck."

When I left you
I didn't know enough about the law
to use it. Just cut and ran.
Put three thousand miles between us.
It was enough.
I was lucky.

Andrena Zawinski

SOME WOMEN TAKE HEART

...I feel the
rage of a soldier standing over the body of
someone sent to the front lines
without training
or a weapon.
—Sharon Olds, "Indictment of Senior Officers"

Some women learn to take it with a stiff
upper lip, stitched up tight, standing up,
right on the kisser, in the teeth, jaw wired,
bruised cheek swollen on a clip under
the eye. Some women take it flat on
their backs, slapped in a cast, choked,
roped in a free-kill-zone, run down out
on the road, statistics in the *Times*.

Some women take it into the heart-
land, run with what they own, new job, new
home, new name in balled fists, chased across
state lines, life on the line—kicked down, kid-
napped, taken back. Some women breathe in
old dreams, slip under the night covers, think
they stink on the sheets, knuckle under
enemy outposts in their minds.

Some women try to make it, fix it, get it
right, can't do anything right—beaten up,
beaten down, beaten to death between thin
walls, windows up. Some women start up
at the door slam, click of the briefcase clasp,

tinkle of ice in the glass, Bourbon splashed
on the floor. Some women can't take any
more morning-after sweet talk, panes out—
board it up, change the locks, bar the doors.

Some women—called ball busters, castrators,
man-haters—stick out their tongues on a dare,
tear in the skin (*this is a pore war*), go for
the muscle and scream: *No more,* bloody
spit ribboning lips, mouthy at the firing line
like they mean it. Some women take
a match to the gas, burn the bed, end up
rattling chains behind bars. Some women
want a revolution like a lover
and a full metal jacket for a heart.*

*"*this is a pore war*" and "*a revolution like a lover*" *are from Robin Morgan's* Monster.

PART THREE
TAKING BACK MY NAME
MOVING BEYOND VIOLENCE

You need only claim the events of your life to make yourself yours. When you truly possess all you have been and done, which may take some time, you are fierce with reality.

—Florida Scott Maxwell
The Measure of My Days

I saw a beggar leaning on a crutch,
He said to me: Why do you ask for so much?
I saw a woman leaning in a door,
She said, Why not, why not, why not ask for more?

—Leonard Cohen
"Bird on a Wire"
(as sung by Judy Collins)

Before today my body was useless.
Now it's tearing at its square corners.
It's tearing old Mary's garments off, knot by knot
and see—Now it's shot full of these electric bolts.
Zing! A resurrection!

—Anne Sexton
"The Kiss"

editor's note

This section of Hard Love *offers an array of writings which describe strategies for defusing intimate violence and moving beyond it. Some authors, like poet Holly Lu Conant Rees, write about escaping, running away, doing whatever it takes to put distance between themselves and the perpetrator. Others, like Jane Steckbeck, Blake More, and Glynnis Reed write about fighting back, retaliating, standing up to the enemy, facing a court battle, and learning self-defense so as to be strong enough to ward off future assaults.*

Through many of the pieces you will read in the following pages it becomes clear that victims must transform themselves into survivors. They must break away from damaging situations and reclaim their own identity, the process described in Sarah Fox's "Taking Back My Name." But the road to recovery is far from easy. As Marilyn Elain Carmen tells us in her essay, it takes a long time and a lot of work. Happily, there are many resources available: community organizations, counselors, spiritual healers, support groups, as well as churches, synagogues and ashrams. But no matter how strong we are, none of these avenues of healing can work without the significant people around us. Several pieces in this section—such as the poems by Barbara Crooker, Judith Neva and Leigh Anne Jasheway—are written in the voice of a friend or family member who stands by the one who is hurt, faithfully offering a pathway out when the time is right.

Once we have escaped, rediscovered our strengths and begun our work toward healing, it is sometimes possible to establish a new relationship built on trust and tenderness. Poets Joseph Millar, Barbara Hendryson and D. M. Wallace focus on some of the intimate acts that can enhance this aspect of healing: crying together, listening to one another, telling everything and rediscovering physical intimacy. However, sometimes, even long after the violence has ended, it still hangs heavily over the survivor's life. Jeff Walt's poem, "This World, This Fracture," captures the persistence of that lingering sorrow with great sensitivity.

*There are many other fine writers in this section whose work embodies the movement toward healing from initmate violence. May their voices inspire you with their promise of hope and renewal. —***E. C.**

Katie Kingston

VOICES

Maybe it's time to take my own voice
out from under the desk. Open it.
But once a voice like that
unleashes, it's impossible to put away.
And the sounds are so unpleasant,
like fingernails on a blackboard moving
upward. And I know it would
eventually get away and find Arla's
voice and Tina's voice. We all
know what a problem a pack can
be, how it moves across the prairie
with its own direction picking up
strays along the way. Until nightfall
when people step out on back porches
to listen, how the howls soar and dive,
ricochet with their own momentum,
how the sky fills with liquid sound,
overflows and floods the empty gullies
with the pure rage of unrestrained water.

Glynnis Reed

DIALECTIC

You heard her
  she's waiting
hanging on for healing words
  that sister
don't have no time
no space within herself
for dangling bitches along a string of
pretty pick-up lines
she been in that flame before
she spit up them burnt alphabets
  before
that guttural language
the won't you come over
spend some time with me
i got beer and a massage-
type dialogue
words that threw themselves up
the morning before
and the night after
she found alphabet-cum all over
her black polyester skirt
No
that sister ain't got no time
for pick-up line ejaculation
she need to hear
some healing words
words she can fold together
and wrap around her like a shawl
she need brothers who come up
knitting the yarn of a loving language
that raises the spirits and
evaporates the caustic asbestos of abuse
she need sage and sincerity
hope and soulful humming
generosity and the genius of
connecting eyes
letting her body alone
be the store of wisdom.

Blake More

COURTROOM C

I sat in a row with others like myself
a straight line facing the judge
waited all morning for her to sign a paper
that promised to protect me from a choice
I'd never really made, from the man
whose shouts still shook my body
whose eyes waited for me in parking lots
and behind the bushes of each step
whose hands drove the car that wanted to run me off the road.

Some clutched babies like kleenex
their features dirty and wrinkled like their clothes
others hauled shadows of a life even more uncertain than before
their black eyes almost eclipsed by black glass
the seamless roots of a fresh dye job
thoughts of a new town, a new start, a place to hide.

Next to them, my kin, I fingered strings of words
the texture of this poem already on my mind
the places I'd seen because of him
not Mexico and Mount Shasta, not even the swingers clubs
but my terrible insides: the part who ran barefoot into the middle
of the night
escaping up hill not down, kimono blown open,
breasts striking the frozen air; the part
who wailed with a voice I'd nearly forgotten
screams that only quieted to shield him from jail;
the part on all fours who scraped across the kitchen floor
grinding raisins and cheerios into naked limbs
anything for freedom.

Looking at them, at myself, I remembered my new home
the one he'd found this morning
rabid face in the backyard, briefcase at his feet
hand braced against the glass, pounding.
Like in Hollywood, I had to find the lock before he did

and, when I did, I fell into the role of hysterical woman
the one who makes me jump up mid-scene and go to the bathroom
raging at the writer, the director, and whoever else
thinks to turn women into such creatures.
I thought of Sheriff Perlow and his careful face
as I described their man: a maniac
wearing a blue suit and purple tie
a hunter who tells blue chip companies
how to spend their billions, who now
as much as ever, was deciding
how
I
lived.

But he would not win and I had the women
around me to prove it, strong, determined
stories imagining themselves one last time
starlight showing me I would not need the shotgun
cradled between me, my stick shift, and the road.

Jane Steckbeck

FIGHTING BACK

I am a sexual assault survivor. I do not feel any shame, embarrassment or humiliation over what happened to me on the bike path. The shame, embarrassment and humiliation belong exclusively to the male who assaulted me.

On September 1, 1995, I left the University of Oregon Law School where I work as a career counselor. I was looking forward to a run on that hot, sunny afternoon—a rare Eugene day. I treasure those days, the sun on my back, the heat pulsating, the sweat running. I decided to run over Autzen foot bridge, through Alton Baker Park, up to Valley River Center. I looked forward to running a new route and seeing how far I could get toward the bridge by Valley River Center. I began thinking as I ran that it would be a nice course to use as a measuring stick for my running progress.

As I ran toward Autzen Foot Bridge, I questioned my choice: after all, I was going to be running on that stretch of path where a woman had been assaulted a year before. I avoided that stretch of path, and had actually never run there. I figured a year later, it would be safe.

As I crossed over the foot bridge, I passed three riff-raffy looking men and I looked each one of them in the eye. One said "Hi" and I said "Hi" back. I imagined what I would do if one lunged out at me. I kept going, on to other thoughts. The day was hot, and I was running well. I kept tabs on my watch, wanting to be aware of when 22 ½ minutes passed, my half-way and turn-around point.

After passing the North Bank office complex, I sized up the path ahead of me. I remember thinking to myself, "If anything happens, I'd be able to get help from the highway," though not in any way conceiving that "anything" might actually happen. I continued running along, checking my watch. I had just looked at my watch as it flashed 21 ½ minutes. I thought to myself that the time had gone fast and it was just about time to turn around.

Somewhere in that thought space, a hand from nowhere clamped forcefully around my mouth. My eyes bulged in shock and disbelief. I was pinned against a person's chest, lifted up to my toes. I remember two distinct voices in my head. On the left side, a voice said calmly and logically, "Jane, it is your turn to deal with this issue." On the right side the voice screamed, "FIGHT!!!!!!!!!!" I recall sort of crumbling forward, at the same time, pulling the hand off my mouth, but this is all a jumble. I began screaming: "Help me, help me," to which a male voice screamed back in my ear: "Shut up! Shut up!" *Like hell I would.* His hand continued to try to cover my mouth, but I was able to keep moving. I continued to struggle and scream and I think I ended up on my back kicking. My attacker pulled off my left running shoe as I kicked. At that moment, I was suddenly free. Bewildered, I looked around for my attacker. Six feet away, on the bike path next to a backpack, was a young male. I glared at him and locked eyes with him, memorizing his face. After about three seconds, the attacker got a strange look in his eyes, something like fear, and he grabbed his pack and turned and ran. Right before he did, I actually had to physically restrain myself from attacking *him,* I was so pumped up with adrenaline, and extremely angry.

I stood still for a second and watched him run away, down the bike path, in the same direction I had come from. It didn't take long for my anger to grow into outrage: *that this loser had grabbed me, that he tried to hurt me, that he could do it to someone else.* I decided that I could not let him get away with what he did to me; I could not leave him out there to do it to someone else who might not be able to fight back. So I decided to chase him. I had a profound sense of knowing that someone would come along who would help me out by detaining the attacker until the police arrived.

I quickly gathered my scattered belongings: bandanna ripped from my head, sunglasses, also ripped from my head, my running shoe. I slipped my shoe on and began chasing the guy. I tried to flag down cars off highway 105, but nobody stopped. I don't know if anyone saw me. *What a lonely experience: tons of people close by, in such isolated little worlds, far too removed to notice or care.* Realizing that my help would not come from the road, I continued my pursuit with vigor.

Becoming the hunter is a fascinating dynamic. My attacker was evidently not in good physical shape, as a little bit of running had him worn out. I had to slow down to keep a safe distance between me and him. He kept looking over his shoulder to see if I was there. The fear was evident. *Tables turned, jerk, how do you like it?*

As he approached the North Bank office complex, two men rounded the corner on mountain bikes. I broke into a sprint and began waving them down and yelling. As they approached, I called out: "Stop that guy, he attacked me!" They turned around immediately and rode up to the attacker. By the time I trotted up, a third man came along on roller blades, with his girlfriend, and he too asked what was going on. When I told him, he grew serious and his face angry. He began to question the guy, and was forceful in convincing him to sit down. A fourth man also rode up, and all closed a circle around the attacker.

One of the original two went to call police at his wife's office at the North Bank office complex.

The police were fantastic and arrived within ten minutes. A female officer arrived first and she placed the guy in handcuffs, then asked me briefly what happened. She then read him his rights. A second officer arrived, and began taking statements from everyone. Finally, he met with me, and had me take him to the spot where I was attacked. It was hard to pinpoint the location. During that time, I discovered an earring was missing: my favorite pair. Small sacrifice, but irritating nonetheless. The officer took a number of photographs; I pointed out my scrapes and scratches, and began noticing a deep soreness in my lower left back. I must have been dropped on my back pretty hard as we struggled, because I remained sore for a month in that spot.

After everyone gave statements and the police were finished, one of the gentlemen who helped me offered to escort me back to the law school. I gratefully accepted. During the trip, he told me that his wife was also a lawyer, and that she had been raped a number of years ago. It was from her office that he made the call. *How many women are similarly scarred?* I wondered.

After getting back to my office, I got on my bike and rode home. I told my husband what happened. He was surprised, angry, and comforting, but seemed awkward and unsure of how to help me. What I think he saw was that I was okay, not too beat up, and so I should be all right. He did his best, but I knew I would need more support. A friend called about that time, so I just blurted it out to her. Wonderful support. Later, I called the Unity Prayer Chain and had a prayer started for the attacker. He's going to need a lot of spiritual help to heal and it is way beyond my control.

That night, when I went to bed, I kept flashing back to the attack, the hand from nowhere, clamping down. I woke Ed up and asked him to talk to me. He pulled me to him, wrapped his arm around me and fell back to sleep. I soon fell asleep and slept just fine. Saturday, I awoke, feeling out of sorts and grumpy. My voice was gone from screaming. It stayed scratchy and husky for three full days. I went to the grocery and noticed with some concern that I was extremely spaced out. When I returned home, I decided that my spaciness was not normal, so I pulled out the Yellow Pages to find out if there was a crisis line. I found the Sexual Assault Support Services (SASS) Hotline and called. I talked to a volunteer for a while, recounting the attack. I found the contact very helpful, though I got tired of the standard "So, how did that make you feel," comments.

I felt better on Sunday, and Monday was a holiday. Tuesday morning at work I got a call from Detective Raney of the Eugene Police Department. He wanted to have me come in for pictures of my bruises and to review my statement. I walked in over my noon hour and a female officer did the photographing. I read the police report and the statements. *Scary*. I am so glad I decided to chase the creep. He told officers *after* they read him his rights that he had intended "to kill [me] then fuck [me]." After reading that, I became convinced that I was put there to stop the guy, because I have the strength and determination. For a while, the words frightened me, but I decided that they were just that: words on paper without any power over me. I now feel only gratitude that I did escape with my life.

On Thursday, September 7, I testified before the grand jury and told them about the attack. I had Triel with me, a volunteer from SASS. It was nice having someone with me to just be there and listen. I was nervous. The D.A. met with me. He gave me a bit of background on the guy, and the expected defense (insanity). He told me a bit about what to expect and reminded me that his job was to get the guy convicted, not to provide emotional support. Had I not been so acquainted with the criminal justice system, I might have been offended; however, my own past experience as a probation officer and attorney gave me realistic expectations about this whole process and the roles of the people involved.

The grand jury issued a four count felony indictment: coercion, assault, attempted rape and attempted murder. *Yowzer*. I was told that I would be advised of future relevant dates.

I began telling more people at the law school about the attack. I wanted to write a piece for the *Dissent*, but was afraid of committing my thoughts to paper: there was a defense attorney whose job it was to get this guy free. Though I could only tell the truth about what happened to me, I knew that this faceless, nameless defense attorney wanted to twist my words, to find something he could use to show something was wrong with me. It was his job; I understood that, but I wouldn't allow him to use me in this way. Finally, a law student offered to write the article for me. I told her my story, she wrote it up. I edited it a bit and it went to print. After that, the outpouring of support was amazing. It felt so good to tell this, over and over: **After I was attacked, I got up off the ground and I chased the man who attacked me and got him locked up! I'm committed to this process so that he is held accountable for what he did to me!!!**

I Read the Following Statement at the Attacker's Sentencing:

I feel like everything I am going to say today is going to sound like a cliché, because I'm sure you've heard it all before. Still, as a critical step in my own healing from this attack, I'm going to say these things anyway.

It is so hard to describe the impact that this violent assault has had on me because there are so many indescribable impacts, so many small shifts in my daily world that are almost impossible to put into words. I'll start with the obvious.

First, there were physical effects. I experienced utter terror and shock when this defendant grabbed me from behind as I jogged, forcefully clamped his hand over my mouth, pinned me to his chest, then yelled at me to "Shut up, shut up," as I screamed and struggled. Next, while I fought with the defendant, I was scraped up and bruised. I had one deep bruise on my lower back that was sore for a month.

Second, while I successfully broke away, a ghost of the physical sensation of being violently grabbed will remain with me for a long while. For the first few nights after the attack, I experienced vivid flashbacks of the attack. I sometimes still hear the defendant's voice yelling in my ear to shut up.

Third, I have experienced a profound loss of my sense of personal safety. This defendant attacked me while I was running in a public area on a sunny afternoon. Now I know there are no safe places for women anywhere, not even in idyllic Eugene.

I look at men differently when I am alone.

I am on edge more, even when my husband and I are walking together through our neighborhood.

I think about being attacked again and how I will respond.

I don't run in my favorite places anymore, which is a loss that may be difficult for others to comprehend.

Though I have taken a self-defense course and plan to continue self-defense training, this cannot replace the security the defendant took when he decided to attack me on September 1.

I feel compelled to address two other points. First, this defendant's mental illness or failure to take behavior controlling medication does not excuse or mitigate his behavior. Choosing not to take medication while knowing the consequences is the equivalent of deliberately choosing those consequences. Likewise, a tragic childhood does not excuse or mitigate his behavior. I could tell this court about some of my own deep psychic wounds suffered at the hands of sick people when I was a child but I won't. The point is: I'm not out victimizing young boys to get even for past hurts. I've dealt with my pain and moved forward. It is time for the defendant to stop using a broken past as an excuse to victimize women in the present.

Second, my level of physical injury and my positive response to this attack should not be considered points in the defendant's favor. When I chose to fight this attacker, then to chase him as he ran off, I did it because I wanted him to be caught and held fully accountable for attacking me. I did not intend for my response to be used as a mitigating factor for *him*. I don't want anyone to forget for one second what he did to me and how it felt. I also don't want anyone to forget that in carrying out this attack, this defendant approached me so quietly from behind that I neither saw nor heard him. I had no warning until his hand slapped over my mouth. My physical wounds from this attack have long since healed. My psychic wounds have a long way to go. I would like to see this defendant serve the maximum sentence possible to impress upon him the seriousness of his conduct and to keep him away from other women for as long as possible. I also want to see the defendant get help: medication, counseling, assistance in finding work and a stable place to live after he has served his time. The defendant has an opportunity here: he can either use this time of incarceration and parole/probation as an opportunity to get help and change or he can blame someone else for this entire situation and grow more pathetic. Let's all hope he chooses the former option.

Now that this whole thing is behind me, I feel the need to move on. I no longer need to continue to tell the world about what happened to me, to talk about it. I do feel the need to continue my self-defense education, whether through another self-defense class, or through a martial art. I know that full healing will be a continuing process.

Elizabeth Claman

THE GINGERBREAD GIRL

I am the gingerbread girl—running
from under the oil slick tongues of sailors,
from the movie mogul with a seminal plot,
from the professor's tome-sized hard-on,
and the psychoanalyst who says he only wants it once
   for my own good.

   Past bridges and airports, past rivers and swamps.
   Along the interstate, and down that old back alley.

In the city I rest, opening my hands for a little mercy.
But every passerby says yummy,
and bites off a finger, until soon I have only palms.
Fine for caressing, but shitty for dialing 9-1-1.

Curled in cardboard I spend the night
thinking of frosting, my tongue to my wrist.
I dream elevator, escalator, fork-lift—any way out.
I dream bran muffin, donut hole, halvah—companions for the road.
They cry with me, and run, licking the tears from my chin.
But in the morning I'm alone with my own wet wrist.

   Cloverleaf overpass.
   Taxi ride, bus ride.
   "What's your hurry?" someone screams.
   But his teeth are long, and time is short.

Back on the road I get thirsty.
(Even gingerbread girls need a little nip sometimes.)
I sit down to rest and crows flock around to peck at my raisin eyes.
I offer my heart instead, but like you, they're greedy.
They want to have their cookie and eat her too.

When I reach Kansas the dust settles
and I meet a man who tells my fortune with wheat.
He says I should get back to basics and do I need his attack dog.
The dog has golden eyes and a tongue of bright red sand paper.
He wags his tail when I talk, but when I touch him, his fur rises.

Just then an agribiz billionaire pulls up in his powder blue Lincoln
and says he has what I need, but I say
"I don't think so," and anyway,
before you know it, I'm in Paris (France, not Texas, thank god),
and the Seine, as polluted as any river, still smells sweet.

In New York I run away from painters,
in Amsterdam, from punks,
in Delphi, from Yanos Achilles,
in Tangiers, from the Djihad.

But being on the road grows weary, so I try to settle down
—with you—the man of my dreams—
you're big and strong and smart and when we make love
real sparks shoot through my brain.

And when we talk, ideas light up like only good ones can.
You even say all those polysyllabic yes words, and know how to tango.
But in the end, I find you only want
what they all wanted—licking the platter clean.

So I pack up my sugar blues,
my few chocolate buttons, my alphabet of nutmeg,
my season of airline tickets, my outbound,
bargain basement gift wrapped in triplicate
white elephant of desire,
and I get back on the road,
only to sing this song again:

  I can run away.
  I can run away.
  I can run away from you, too.

Holly Lu Conant Rees

LAST REFUGE

eight days now, in his distant
cabin where she's finally
come to ground, time counted
in the moon's height
and the precise deep chill
which gathers just before
darkness lifts. the first
dilated night, she'd left
his radio on and hissing,
voices weak and shallow
as hers if she'd thought
to speak. now, she keeps
the black stove stoked
for the glow in its belly
and its steady human hum.
in such wide silence,
she listens to what's
already been said, without
the decoration of face
or touch. she ladles
black savory tea
from the standing pot
into her one cup
and spiral vapors heat
her face like breath.

nearly living here, she wishes
a woman had made this home,
which gives shelter without
comfort. there could be colored
glass, open to the pouring
sun (and unbroken
snowy wind)—an Irish
loft (and risky edges)
tucked round with down
and flannel—bright oak
(and tarry boots) in planned
patterns across the floor.
she's been only a visitor
in this dim cell, between

these rough scabby walls,
on the heaped pallet
which smells of oil
and cold ash. as she slides
home the pine bolt,
she see his hands, fisted
around a hammer
or her wrist, driving
in a dry fury against
a wall he never had
the skill to build.

the weather's turned.
the last salty porridge bubbles
and spits on the stove, the last
dry wood sprawled by the door.
she's been hauling water,
scraping the bucket across
the slow creek, stirring away
the thin scrim of ice,
her sleeves sodden
and murky. she's sluiced out
the tin basin, rinsed hot
water through her nightclothes,
hung to dry by the breathing
stove. water breaks
into steam with the crisp
rattle of hail dropping
on the frozen grass.
she pours what's boiled
into the vat, and heat
leaches into the dark
gathered water. she scours
her cracked skin, rinses
her stripped hair. no heat
reaches the shaking chill
in her chest. all her flesh
dizzy and swollen beneath
her stiff gown, she's laid
out on icy, familiar ground,
brilliant cold climbing
up through her as night
closes round, and still,
warm as she's ever been.

Marilyn J. Boe

WHAT WE SAVE, WHAT WE THROW AWAY

I empty this basket full
of get-well cards, letters, many writing
what they've never told me,
eye to eye, phone to phone—
        a son's suicide
        a mother's alcoholism
        a father's mental illness.
Their pens against paper unlock
that private place saved for sadness.
They share their private hell to heal mine
after reading of my injuries:
"Mother Stabbed by Daughter,"
trusting me with details of their lives
the way you trust someone
to understands pain
who's had the same operation,
or has walked guarded years around
a schizophrenic.

I read them all again,
then throw each one away.
I'm not the same person I was then
and neither are they.

Andrea King Kelly

HOMECOMING

In the hospital
I am obsessed
with lips, my own
swollen over my teeth
like a minstrel man's.
With a tube
of Coming Up Roses,
I paint them on everything:

big red smackers
on the bathroom mirror,
thick valentines
around the bruises
on my arms and hips.
Even my thighs
exchange symmetrical kisses.

Before they send me
home to you again,
I want a new name.
My own is a harsh
three-syllable thrust,
a dark misnomer
that rings through the angry house.

I want to come home
a Lisa or a Sarah,
a different woman
with a gentle name,
sacred as the last word
on a man's lips.

Sarah Fox

TAKING BACK MY NAME

When a woman tells the truth she is creating
the possibility for more truth around her.
—Adrienne Rich

I was 20 and too drunk to live
with my parents any longer
so I and my cat and our stuff, crammed into a City
Vet cab, moved into your one room, roach-
in-toothbrush, Cocaine Larry across the hall,
N 21st St apartment the day before Thanksgiving
in 1987. I needed a care-
giver. You invited us kindly but then began taking
the job too seriously, rearranging
your tone and the weather
in the room when I called the wrong
friend or played my harmonica
or mentioned that I wanted to read
Duras. You were smarter than
me, you said. You left for two
nights the time I wore lipstick
to hear Allen Ginsberg read "Sunflower Sutra."
But where could I go? So
I quit drinking (though you were
a bartender) and tried hard to believe
you and believe in you. "We're not
conventional people," you said.
It used to sound so heroic.

Before we got married I practiced writing
it and signing it on spare pieces
of paper at work and in the kitchen:
Sarah Wynn, Mrs. Sarah F. Wynn.
After the 3 minute ceremony
in San Francisco, I stared at it
weird as a foreign stamp
on the credit card receipt
for crab legs and egg rolls at Hunan Home
(you were still complaining
about the middle initial on the Certificate of Holy
Matrimony). It never sounded right—

Sarah Wynn—no
grips for the mouth to get hold of.

But you re-worked my skin
with it, changed my antennae: your name
on your 4 AM knuckles, on the soles
of your shoes, on the after dinner
garbage you liked to dump
over my head. Your name
on the checkbook, on every missed
Thanksgiving dinner and period,
on your father's union card and on
all his fathers' gravestones. Between
the lines your name in the "FUCK
YOU BITCH" and "STUPID CUNT" and "I HATE
YOU I HATE YOU I HATE
YOUR GUTS." Your name
married also the key that screamed
in the door, on the doors that slammed and
your name all over the empty
barefoot locked out of the house
backyard half-dead crabapple nights.
Your name on the medical record
file which holds my x-rays for
a fractured jaw and a bruised nose
when I told them
I "fell while dancing."
Your name on your spit in my hair.
Your name on my shattered guitar.
Your name on the mailbox and the disconnected
telephone. Your name on the drawn shades,
on every brick bricking in the entire
last noise of our house.

On the birth certificate and social security
card of the daughter whose
body drank and grew from my body
and whose joints rollerpinned across my
roundness in the quiet, safe
bath nights you worked late;
the daughter who cleaved her milk-
strong muscles through the horrible,

weeping tunnel of my body inside the cave
where we alone were making life
while you scoffed and slept
in a corner: your name.
Your name even now on the loud
blue distance in her eyes that she
learned by heart from
your face for her own.

The day after I left
for good I told the attorney I needed
my old name back, first thing.
We couldn't find it anywhere,
not even on my driver's license
or my fingers or my tongue.
But I'm going to
sing it, sing it back from you: *Mrs. Wynn*

Mrs. Sarah F. Wynn
    Sarah Wynn
        Sarah W
            Sarah Wife
                Sarah Whore
                    Sarah Witch
                        Sarah Woman
                             Sarah F
                                   Sarah Face
                                        Sarah Flower
                                            Sarah Ferocious
                                                  Sarah Fox

                                                 Sarah Elizabeth, who is

daughter to Susan Irene
who was born to Marie
whose mother was Dorie
who came to Anna
who was daughter to Mary
whose wife was Eve
who is sister to
me who is
Sarah.

Rebecca Whetstine

SUBTLE JOY

There is a peaceful atmosphere in our shelter. We women have made a nice home. The kitchen is clean, the food cooked is generally good, getting better as we go away from frying and move into sautéed mushrooms, salads, rice. Settling into each other. The population has waxed and waned, and still, we who came in at the same time, we are here together.

Every one has their share of trouble, perhaps more. Some of the children have been molested: they exhibit marker behaviors. Two of them are chronic and inveterate liars. The tattling and crying is constant. My child picks up tattling, experimenting with it. Tries on talking back to see if it can fit into his own repertoire. My response, of course, is unequivocal. I am not happy that he is surrounded by these behaviors in chronic form, and yet we have all made our peace with it and somehow manage all of our children.

Shelby is the first to find a home. She is so lonely she comes back for dinner, hangs around. She brings several of the women to her house for the night. This says sad things for the isolation and poverty she lives in, good things for the way we have become an integrated household caring each for our own and one for another.

Dinner done, I climb the stairs to my little room. Windows open to the street sounds and the breeze. Art postcards on the wall over my makeshift desk with the word processor. Crates for shelves and candles lit. The room is fragrant. Calm. The gentle strobe of the candles and the underscent of hot wax is delicate, a discrete reminder of the fine-ness of life as I like it.

My son and I carry the candles into my shower. He asks me to put them just so. We stand in the shower together, motionless, not speaking. He is truly my son: we just feel the warm water, feel the candle light, feel the quiet and the not-moving. I know he feels it too, for he speaks first and tells me:

"Mama, isn't this nice?"

"Yes, son. Just feeling the water pour down, hunh?"

"Yes. Let's just keep it quiet."

He shifts around the shower, stands with his face to the glass door, head against the wall. After several more minutes, he moves across to the back of the shower and stands where there is no water, face to the wall. He is feeling-sensing, and I am too. We are doing it together.

Subtle joy. His spirit is alive, intact. He connects still. And I do too.

Mind quiet, I watch cabbages and roses shift and settle in the glass patterns of the door. Touch my boy's shoulder, barely. And out of the depths of his little-big being comes this:

"Mama, I *love* you."

And from mine:

"And *I* love *you*."

LESLIE, REVEALED

There's this hardcore girl here in the shelter, a windstorm on the run, passing through. Been through every kind of twist the evil spirit can put on a woman: rapes, beatings, Turned Out to terror as a baby girl. Sold to a pimp by her sister while still little. Cut, bruised, dishonored and betrayed. Mother taking her beautiful mixed-blood child. Turned her out too. Fast life, pimped hard enough to supply the $500 a day habit and a Lincoln Towne Car. I have avoided her tale for hours, knowing that something heavy and knowledgeable in me will press on my soul.

I am tired, scattered, yearn for a compassionate, conscious touch. I feel as though I cannot carry another's burden. The burden of being one who knows, one who will not avoid or forget. I know that if I let her talk, I will carry her with me.

And yet I do it: I let her talk it. I stand as she comes into my face—intense, dark, beautiful—and tells it. She bumps auras with me, but never collides—we do not melt together, but somehow share the same space. "Integrated," she says, lacing her slender fingers. I feel her mind: alive, sharp, grasping—native intelligence and a fine point that must be worked.

And I am looking at myself. My god, we are kin. I look at her, and do not see the thickening calves, the tangled hair. I look at her and it is the wild, dark, powerful spirit of her that I receive. She is magnetic, muscular, constant motion. She is big, hot, a ride in the hurricane to be with her.

She shifts lexicons and body language as I let her follow me about. She blocks my way as I move toward the door of the kitchen. She is a stout slice of life: behind the affirmations and the sisterhood I hear the hard player, the angry whore betrayed. Again. I know how it is to play the role set before me in defiance of the role. *You want a hot bitch, I will give you the hottest bitch you ever...*

I watch her bring forth her story to me, I watch microsecond performance art as she slips through time, bending dimensions to get at the message pressing out of her deep places.

Sense is trying to make itself, cannot quite get through. Keep talking, another try...

She can love. She attracts sadists and Real Men. She frightens off the men of little substance. She chooses the sadists time and time again, matching wits and spirit force with the evil that brought her blood to the surface. We live so close to the surface, she and I. Menstrual blood, passionate rutting love. Giving it all to get something. Can't decide whether it is a tender father or a wrestling match we want. Giving it all: to get something.

Judith Neva

HELPING MY DAUGHTER PACK

We've done this before—cushioned
the fragile things, lamps,
the frosted swan—in the move

from father to husband, from
abuse to abuse, three times
and back, or from Butte

to here and now
you are Somewhere Else,
moving from box to box

in a daze and I see you
walking through lanes
of blossoming cherry trees,

your flower basket full,
wearing a red skirt,
and a rose pinned in your hair.

And I can't ask
why you run
three thousand miles

away from yourself and I know
you'll be back for your children,
your cat. Take my credit card,

a new clutch for your car,
a hundred bucks.
You've already got

my bangle earrings,
and my tambourine.

Leigh Anne Jasheway

JUST BETWEEN FRIENDS

You say you're going back to him today
he finally called
and said you could come home
no demerit no penalties no hard feelings
he knows you know
you were wrong
and that's why he had to hit you.

You leave your rumpled bedclothes
        hanging from my couch
gather together your blue jeans and socks and panties
wrap your toothbrush in Saran Wrap
retrieve your Morning Thunder from the pantry
and toss them all in your still
half-packed suitcase.

You are ready.

I hug you good-bye
then reach down
to pick up some invisible item from the floor
before I come to tears again,
mumbling that you are always welcome
  here
to this way station in the night
more to the carpet than to you.
You have already left
even as you stand at the door
half-in   half-out.

I should shake you, slap you, shout at you
show you the patterns of your existence
the comings and goings
and running from the ones who love you
to the ones who are willing to forgive you.

But I don't.
That's his style, not mine
although I am tempted.

But I am just your woman friend
not your lover
what we have is just between friends
and cannot compete with the mystery
that occupies your eyes whenever you think of him,
like now.

And so you go.
I smile and tell you how happy I am for you,
glad that you've worked it out.
I will stock up on kleenexes
and move the phone
next to my bed
just in case . . .

You know.

Barbara Crooker

FOR A FRIEND WHO THINKS ABOUT GOING BACK TO HER ABUSIVE HUSBAND WHEN THE NIGHTS ARE LONG AND COLD AND PAYCHECKS DON'T MEET EXPENSES

On the hill behind our house,
a tractor has harrowed the cornfields,
stripped the skin off the land,
turned it inside out, a rich dark corduroy.
And you have turned your life around,
left the husband who beat you
with a wine bottle, smashed the thermostat
to save heat, hit your children
with words, followed us on our weekend runs
in case we met with secret lovers.
You've flown north to New Hampshire,
to the White Mountains, where snow
still blankets the woods,
while here we're stripping for spring.
You've left behind your worldly goods,
tangled in a web of litigation,
but your life is now your own.
Tundra swans stopped here this week
on their way to the Arctic, paused
a few days to peck and glean the cornfields.
Soon, they'll spread their wings,
white whistling sails,
fly off to the northern rim of the world.
Now, you fly, stay free.

WHY YOU DON'T HAVE TO BE AFRAID TO LIVE ALONE, I TELL MY FRIEND, THE BATTERED WIFE

Stripping and waxing the kitchen floor
on a Saturday night, alone,
waiting for my divorce to become final,
scraping off years of built-up accumulus—
that week, at a party, I met
the man who would become my lover,
but that was in the future—
now, as the wax came off
in yellow patches, the dark dirty rinse water
swirled in the drain, all I knew
was that my life had opened up again,
stretched before me with its infinite possibilities.
The waxed floor shone like a silver pond in the moonlight.
I had never been so happy.

Willa Schneberg

HOTEL ROOM

Stay out. I have the chain on the door.
The DO NOT DISTURB sign on the knob. I am
wearing a new nightgown for me, not for you.

I tear the thin strip over the toilet seat
in half. Remove the glass from its paper
wrapper, fill it with booze, ice and
toast to anonymity.

I place my watch on the night table.
Magic Fingers massage my back.
I no longer feel your breathing outside the door.
I don't worry about you or the others,
because tonight we are strangers.
Until check-out time tomorrow I'm nobody's
wife, mother, sister, daughter, neighbor.

I'm Jane Doe, the guest in room 361,
who doesn't have to empty lunch boxes of
gooey white bread and can watch TV
until the star-spangled banner waves.

Marilyn Elain Carmen

THERE IS SUCH STRENGTH WITHIN THE BEAUTY AND FRAGILITY OF A ROSE, OTHERWISE HOW COULD IT RETURN SUMMER AFTER SUMMER?

The issue of violence, abuse, battering has been such a central part of my life up until the last five years that I am now sometimes amazed and always relieved that my life is now free of this horror. I am now forty-eight years old, and I as I look back, I realize that the torture I endured and accepted did not start with any of my three husbands, or the other men in my past. Those years of abuse provided me with a link to my battered childhood. I was "at home," I was "comfortable" in situations of abuse.

As a child, I was physically, psychologically, and sexually abused by my mother, my aunt, and her son, from the time I was about three years old until my mother died when I was eleven. The physical and psychological abuse continued when I went to live with my father and step-mother, though to a lesser degree.

Of course, then, after such an upbringing, it was only "natural" for me to "seek out" a man who would continue the abuse that was my way of life. I always found one. It wasn't difficult. Almost like I wore a sign that read "Kick me—I'm available." The first one was Harold. I was eighteen. A virgin. He convinced me, not long after we met, to have sex with him. He would say, ever so sweetly, "Don't worry about getting pregnant. My mother will love you. She will help with the baby." That was what I wanted to hear. I was so hungry for a mother. I so wanted a family. A little baby. Someone to love. Someone to love me. I was thrilled when the doctor—after getting an extra feel and commenting on how soft and juicy I felt—told me I was pregnant. (The dirty ol' bastard.) Harold and I were together on and off for the next four years. I conceived four times. Three children were born, one miscarried.

Harold's abuse started before my first child, Michele, was born. I was about five months pregnant, and as I moved to get out of his brother's car, I felt a sharp sting across my face. I don't remember the incident that led up to Harold's smacking me, but I know I was shocked and humiliated.

The fights continued. He stayed out for days at a time, and when he did come home there would be no paycheck. No money. Many were the times when I'd go to his job to get some money before it evaporated, only to have him tell me that the checks didn't come in that day or that the boss died before he signed the checks. Of course, when he got home I'd be upset. An argument would occur, and I'd end up with a black eye, or perhaps he'd knock me to the floor, sometimes bruising my back that has been constantly sore since I had open-heart surgery at the age of seventeen.

I'll never forget the time when I was eight months pregnant with my second child. Harold and I were both standing in the bedroom. Again, we were arguing about something. I don't remember what, probably money or his women. He had the habit of telling me that he used "Long Stay" for his women. When I asked him what that was, he told me, "It keeps me from coming so fast when I'm screwing. I don't need to use it for you though." Anyhow, that day in the bedroom, with my belly almost to the floor, he slapped me so hard in the back that I fell to the floor. Right after that, I had to be rushed to the hospital. John, my first son, was born one month early. He weighed 4 pounds and thirteen ounces. He is now 27.

After another child was born, I finally left Harold for good. But, you know, it really did not make that much of a difference. I continued to seek out man after man that would abuse me in one way or another. I was looking so desperately for a father, a mother, looking for someone to love me. What I continually found, though, was someone to treat me as I had been treated as a child. A horrible circle.

Many of these relationships or one-night stands are nothing but a blur to me now. I was in a constant state of search. I was also in a constant state of being high. I abused prescription and over-the-counter drugs and alcohol for about fifteen years. On weekends, sometimes even during the week, I went from bar to bar, leaving my babies with almost anybody, at times, even leaving them alone. Always searching. In all fairness to myself, I should mention that there were many times during this period of my life when I had to work two, even three jobs to hold things together. Once I was a waitress in a bar, my favorite place, or so I thought. Only God took care of my babies in those days. I worked every weekend, three nights for $15.00, plus tips. I got very little tip money because I was too tired after working at a typewriter all week to smile, and the men did not tip or ask to take you home if you didn't smile.

I did find another husband in a bar, though. My third. He, too, was so nice at first, especially when he found out that I was buying the house that I lived in with my three children. He thought that I had money. What a joke. How foolish of me. I was soon to find out that he was just as abusive as the other men in my life, both psychologically and physically, perhaps even more so.

We had enormous fights every weekend. I'd end up with black eyes, skinned knees, bruised shoulders. There were always marks on my body. Swollen lips. It was a natural state. Some of the scars are still visible after almost fifteen years. Oh, I wouldn't just stand there and let him hit me. I'd fight back. But I could never win. How in the Hell could I? I wasn't strong enough. And it would always end up with me abusing myself some more with drugs and alcohol.

In those days, I turned everything in on myself. I punished myself for everything. I was the guilty one, so I made sure that I found someone to make me pay for my guilt.

As I analyze my life now with my own self-help techniques, such as yoga and meditation, reading, writing, or the help of a counselor or friend, I have come to find, through many of my moments, a certain inner peace, a calmness. I am learning that I can control my life, up to a certain point. I do not want to give the impression that I have let my abusers "off the hook," so to speak. This is certainly not the case. They were at fault, and I hate the things that they did to me. I hate the things I allowed them to do to me. I am now learning, though, to give up my role as victim. I am learning to build my own inner strengths. I have begun to look at myself very intently in the mirror, not to see how attractive I am, but to try to see what is really *within* the image I see. Something occurred to me the other day. I realized that I look very fragile, very gentle, almost like I'll break in half if someone slams a door around me. When I discovered this, I went into the kitchen and discussed it with my youngest daughter, Crystall. She said, "Yes, Mommie, you do look fragile. Very fragile."

There is nothing I can do to change the way I look. And I would have no desire to do so, even if I could. But what I can do is to continue to realize that I have power and strength within myself, within my soul. I know that I will never enter into another abusive or demeaning relationship. Really, what it is that comes to me as I write this is that I have given up looking for the abuse I endured as a child. What happened to me as a child was wrong, and I no longer need to live that way. I also know that it will be a daily struggle to maintain my sense of power and to render those powerless who abused me as a child.

Jeff Walt

THIS WORLD, THIS FRACTURE

She walks the dirt road
her grandmother walked, picks
apples from the trees
her father planted as a boy,

and visits the farmhouse
where her brother lives, where his wife
bleeds constantly from between her legs,
until now, *the end,* where she is empty

as a beehive in winter, and reaches
into a pocketbook of photos
when the pain becomes too much.
They take care of each other.

She knows this world better
than she knew her husband, his arm
a crowbar across her chest, the all night
games of poker where she played

the barmaid, the whore—"For keeps!"
He'd scream when he ran out of dimes
and quarters. Now she lies awake
listening to the stars, remembering

the son who cried for her at the bus stop
and now as he makes love to his new girlfriend
in the next room. She thinks of the fresh sheets
she put on his bed, the girl's wet center.

She remembers the word *love,*
before the world rose up around her
and fractured. She wants to live.
She wants to sleep in this bed forever;

wants the knock-knock-knock of her son humping,
his headboard bruising the wall.
Her sister-in-law still holding on.
She wants the smell of hot baked bread

until they smooth the earth over her grave,
the plot beside her husband, down the road
where she ran from him to her own mother's
tombstone; the graveyard where she played

Doctor and drank beer and sang hymns
in her best Sunday dress: where she listened
to her brother call her name from their childhood
house, her father's belt coiled

around his adult fist,
the steady blows, and that young voice
of her only sibling: shrill as a girl
chased in a game of Tag on a playground,

loud enough to be remembered still,
lunging like a dog where she lay
silent in the wet grass,
the sun and moon framed in the same sky.

THE SMELL OF SEX

I am sure there is a word for this
but it is not *love*
that moves my hand across his body
like the heart of a ouija board
pushing toward fate in darkness
sliced by the moon's greasy,
blue afterglow on our bones
smoothed into tight hospital corners
around our slick bodies.
Late August night wets our sex.
I think of how the smell
fertilizes the plums,
brings them into full bloom
so they hang like testicles,
their sweetness like his sweetness
only without the repetition of desire.
The stars blink because the stink
of our sex irritates their eyes,
and the bats squawk like children drowning,
swoop from the rafters after the smell.
Even the moths that chatter
at the window screen smell our sex
because we are lit from inside
with constant desire.
How odd? I think, to hear kids
on the streets.
How can they go on playing
children's games with the smell
chasing them? Especially
when just tonight the plums
are coming into full bloom
and sweet desire has bruised
my lips and swells in my lucky mouth.

Dorianne Laux

ENOUGH MUSIC

Sometimes, when we're on a long drive,
and we've talked enough and listened
to enough music and stopped twice,
once to eat, once to see the view,
we fall into this rhythm of silence.
It swings back and forth between us
like a rope over a lake.
Maybe it's what we don't say
that saves us.

AFTERWARDS

when we sat side by side
on the edge of the unmade bed,
staring blindly at our knees, our feet,
our clothes stranded in the middle of the floor
like small, crumpled islands,
you put your arm around my shoulder
in that gesture usually reserved
for those of the same sex—equals,
friends, as if we'd
accomplished something together,
like climbing a hill or painting a house,
your hand at rest over the curved bone
of my shoulder, my loud nipples
softening into sleep.
Stripped of our want, our wildness, we sat
naked and tired and companionable
in the sleek silence, innocent
of what we'd said, what we'd done,
our breath slowing, our heads tipped
and touching at the crown,
like a couple of kids
slumped on a dock in the sun,
our legs dangling above the bright water,
admiring each other's reflections.

Sheila S. Velazquez

THE MATTRESS

"You should probably take the old set out first." The woman stood in the doorway as the men approached the house.

"Yes ma'am," said the one closest to her. He was big and blond-haired, wearing overalls and a t–shirt. The other man was younger, black, with bony knees protruding through the holes in his jeans.

She led them to the bedroom, pointed to the bed stripped to reveal the faded mattress.

The woman felt uncomfortable having these men enter her room. For one thing, she had not had a man in here in years. No male scents or sounds in her bedroom for a long time. For another thing, it was early morning, and she had not washed, or brushed her teeth either. The clothes she had worn yesterday as she pulled weeds from the garden, these were the ones she had on now. They were dirty, and she didn't like anyone to see her like this. But the men didn't seem to notice. *I guess they see everything,* she thought.

Yesterday, in the furniture store, she had tested the new mattress. It was firm and cushy—no lumps. The saleswoman had asked her if she wanted stain repellant applied.

"No need for that," she had answered.

"I know what you mean," said the other woman. "Sure wish they had it when I was younger though." They had laughed.

The men slid the old mattress along the bare wood floor and then lifted it carefully into the truck. She wondered about that. *I guess they felt something special about mattresses. So much of life happened on them. And they all ended up at the dump.*

The woman stepped out into the cool morning and leaned against the woodpile while the men went back for the old box spring. She snapped a twig from a log and scraped garden soil from under her fingernails.

She thought about the mattress. Sad to let it go. But it hurt her back now. No sense holding onto pain. Pain. There had been pain on that mattress, years of it. Midnight fights. Crying herself to sleep after he rolled over and shut her out. Fights about money, sex, all of it. And rape. Not date rape, or stranger rape, but marital rape. Just as painful, more humiliating. one time he had come in drunk and flipped the mattress, with her on it, to the floor. She had hit her head on the corner of the nightstand. Things were real bad then. She had thought about keeping the hunting rifle in her closet, but the gun disappeared. He knew what she was thinking.

Long before that, the bed had been her heaven at the end of the day. Long kisses and intense passion on the mattress. His hard, muscled legs had bent over her as his tongue and hands caressed her. No words though. He never said the words. She had often wondered if it mattered that it was her.

Children were conceived on the mattress. And comforted after bad dreams, and read to. When they were sick, she sometimes let them stay in the big bed. Now she shared it with the cat, who left black hairs on the patched white sheets.

"Got the Ecstasy model, huh?" said the blond man. "Sure is pretty. High too. lambswool in the cover. Bet you're gonna sleep good tonight."

They carefully ripped the plastic from the new pieces and placed them on the bed. The top of the mattress was waist high. She laughed, "It's the Princess and the Pea bed. I'll need a ladder to get onto it. And God help me if I ever fall."

The men collected the plastic wrappings and cord and retraced their steps back to the kitchen.

"Want some coffee?"

They looked at each other, and the black man said, "Sure is nice of you, Ma'am." It was the first he had spoken since coming into the house.

"Well, sit down then," she said. She took two big mugs from the shelf. one was chipped. She rinsed the cup she had been using herself and replaced the chipped one with it. The pot was nearly full; she always made too much coffee. But today she was glad she had it to offer.

The men added sugar and milk and then sat quietly sipping. Then the black man spoke. "Ma'am, I wonder if... could I have your permission to take the old set home? My kids ain't got no bed good as that, and I sure would be grateful."

She nodded, forming a mental picture of his house, his kids. How good could they have it, him making minimum probably, worse off than her even.

They finished the coffee, and said thanks again. The young black man smiled and tipped an imaginary cap to her.

She watched from the doorway as they laid the plastic wrapping from the new mattress on the floor of the truck. Then, they carefully set the old box spring down and placed the mattress on top. The black man patted the mattress and smiled at her as the truck rolled down the driveway.

Janine Canan

OFFERING MY TEARS

Here are my tears, tall pitchers of tears.
I pour them round you,
so you may grow more and more beautiful.

The cedar offers its sheltering arms,
the house its shield from piercing winds.
The sky offers its lumined breath,
the crow its urgent call.
So I offer these salty tears,
wept from the boundless ocean of love.

Pitchers and pitchers of shining tears—
as I pour them
may I grow more and more aware.

MY TREASURE BOX

Your nightmares will always be safe
in my treasure box: fine metal painted
with colorful blossoms and birds.

Your nightmares belong with the jewels
you gave me: carnelian dream,
melting amber, lapis studded with golden stars.

There whenever anyone cries
Nobody loves me: rivers run turquoise,
hearts are ruby, mirrors reflect only beauty.

Joseph Millar

LISTENER

The woman with her face pressed
against my chest and both legs
locked around my knee, breathing deeply,
has floated into some quiet stream
swaying past its wooded banks without me.

Somehow I've told her everything
whispered it through my cracked voice
into the stillness around her
as we sat together in the gloom
waiting for the movies to begin,
and later by the bridge
watching dim surf ignite offshore.
In this bed I've exploded
each grief into her body,
one by one, until they came loose:
the drinking, the failed marriages and jobs,
the weight of my children pressing me down.

There must be some kindness
I could bring to her dream now,
listening to her breath
unwind in the small room
and wishing I had never hurt anyone.
What still country have I come to,
where the long grass bends
under the animals when they lie down
emptied of suffering?
What slow river flows
beneath her forehead, the secret
petals of her ears
adrift in the auburn hair,
gathering darkness?

D. M. Wallace

ALL THE MEN I KNOW

need to cry, and do,
as if their lives depended,
their wounds opening soft
and wide as my own sex,
wet with longing as they are
with sorrow. With the gift
of my kind I make a window
or a mirror. I come to imagine
I carry some cruel but necessary
rod within me, a wand which
opens and reopens their oldest,
youngest fear. In the harsh
light of their grief I disappear
and for a brief time find
my own release, just listening
as a shell listens to the sea,
a small bird to the wind.
I hover cool and sexless
over these, the lovers
and the loved, who need
to cry, for their kind.

Barbara Hendryson

UNTIL EACH MOVES NEARLY TO THE OTHER

We turn in the darkness.
Nothing to hear
except our breaths
reeling in and out
of our bodies.

Everything
that can be said
has been spoken,
each word fallen
careless as spit seeds.

Our bodies twice
cleave the bed,
a dark rise between.
Too much has passed
for the loss of one sigh.

We lie, and wait—
each for a signal
from the other;
for the least warmth
drifting over the rise.

I feel you stretch
the way a boy in a movie show
will twist and yawn,
extending his arm
across the narrow beauty

of his girl's shoulders,
she shifting and leaning
nearly into its curve.
I turn, facing the gesture
I perceive to be

your offered penitence,
and in this way
make my own.
Your hand falls on my waist;
mine on the long roped

plane of your thigh,
rough texture of skin.
Your sad fingers trail
my face, while mine graze
the hardness of your arm . . .

and so on, until each moves
nearly to the other—
the way common air necessarily
joins the clay of our bodies . . .
the way it heals.

PART FOUR
DARNING THE WORLD
A JOURNEY OF TRANSFORMATIONAL HEALING

Rise up, my love, my fair one, and come away.
For lo, the winter is past, the rain is over and gone;
The flowers appear on the earth;
The time of the singing of birds is come,
And the voice of the turtle is heard in our land.

—*the* Song of Songs

Earth's crammed with heaven,
And every common bush afire with God;
But only he who sees takes off his shoes . . .

—Elizabeth Barrett Browning
"Aurora Leigh"

Nonviolence can never be absolute. But we can continue to do our best to minimize the harm we cause and to maximize our appreciation and reverence for all life—people, animals, plants, and minerals.

—Chân Không
"Commonly Asked Questions,"
For a Future to Be Possible

editor's note

The authors whose works you will read in this section share their experiences of transformation, transcendence, tenderness, joy and delight. They affirm life and celebrate intimacy. Rather than answering violence with violence, they offer hope for our culture by expressing its most positive aspects: friendship, familial closeness, delight in the natural world, sensual love and spiritual awakening. From Dorianne Laux's humorous celebration of kissing to D. M. Wallace's poems about Eros in all its forms; from Hannah Wilson's gentle meditations to Amy Klauke-Minato and Elizabeth Sinclaire's visions of the natural world, these authors write about a healing intimacy that is both moving and inspiring. John R. Campbell's observations on parental love in his essay, "Domestic Waters," have renewed my belief in family as a vital possibility. And Yvonne Vowels' candid description of her journey toward enlightenment and love has inspired me to deepen my own spiritual explorations.

Each time I read Kim Addonizio and Alice Evans' beautiful poems about their daughters, Laure-Anne Bosselaar's wise "Inventory," Jeff Walt's tender "Afternoon on the Stoop," and Emily Robertson's idyllic "Love Tells Her Story," I am reminded that despite the pain, sorrow, greed and violence that mar our world we do have a lot to celebrate. I am grateful for all of the voices in this section, for their heroism, depth and resiliency. They remind me of the many modes of healing that are available to all of us, and the many ways there are to celebrate life. As Thich Nhat Hanh teaches, "When we appreciate and honor the beauty of life, we will do everything in our power to protect all life." That is the ultimate message of this anthology. —**E.C.**

Kim Addonizio

CRANES IN AUGUST

They clutter the house,
awkwardly folded, unable
to rise. My daughter makes
and makes them, having heard
the old story: what we create
may save us. I string
a long line of them over
the window. Outside
the grey doves bring
their one vowel to the air,
the same sound
from many throats, repeated.

THE TASTE OF APPLES

All morning my daughter has been picking apples.
She brings them in a brown paper sack,
she is happy, she offers me one.
A while ago, thumbing through an early
Life magazine, I came across a photograph—
a solemn group of schoolchildren—and thought
of what time does, of how their faces
must have changed as the photographer finished
and they broke from their neat rows,
became men, women, old.
My oblivious child empties her sack
into my lap... For the rest of the day
she plays quietly, moves them from room to room
with her dolls and animals, at last arranges them
in tender patterns on the rug.
Now, late at night, I want to write something
that can be offered, taken, eaten. If I say
window, sky, white apple, if I think of a black branch
bending but not breaking, will I have said
what I mean—that tonight, as I watched her
smoothing out a dress for morning, carefully,
before she turned her face up for a kiss, I knew
she had already gone from me, into her life. Children
in a photograph, the tart sweetness
of apples, my daughter's fingers
grimy with soil and smelling of her sex.
She mutters in her sleep. I keep
a bowl on the kitchen table, filled now
with apples, the hard, shiny fruits
I will bite into, one by one, savoring each.

Alice Evans

IN THESE GENTLE YEARS

Here at the abandoned school
my daughter plays alone
skipping from slide
to swings to seesaw,
finding balance
in movement.

I'm not in the mood
for playing, we have biked
here together, that is enough.
I companion her by watching.

I also watch crows
strut across dry fields,
scuttling their claws
through straw and dirt,
searching for dead beetles,
a lizard's brittle tail.

I could ask for something more,
but I believe
I've got more than I deserve.
No one hunts my heart
for tomorrow's meal.
I can no longer feel the slice
of a hunter's indifferent claw.

I have skipped my way
past all that,
swung out beyond
their reach, seesawed
my way into balance.

In these gentle years
I make do

with more than I once had,
less than I dreamed of,
exactly what I've got.

When my daughter
reaches the merry-go-round
I rise
to push her
in circles.

Elizabeth Claman

AT THE MOVIES

for my daughter

I watched, as you opened the car door and ran toward the theater, moved by your straight, small back. Two dollars clutched to your chest, seven years old and ready, you announced, for a matinée alone. The marquee neon jigged and underneath, you waved good-bye. But at the window, two older boys shoved you aside, the ticket seller unable to see. They bought tickets, punching one another's shoulder. You turned toward me for a moment, eyes stunned, and I imagined leaping from my car and chasing them, hurling them to the ground and screaming until they curled in fear. As I opened the car door, ready to spring, the taste of their blood on my tongue, you bought your ticket and walked inside, ponytails innocent of defeat. I stayed a long time in the car, wondering if I should follow you, sit through this movie I saw nine times as a child, lurk two rows back to keep you safe. I imagined you at 12, at 17, at 35, alone in the dark with your popcorn and bonbons, and me behind you, watching those movies again and again. Breathing in your laughter and your tears, I would guard the seats to your left and to your right so that no one could get close enough to harm you.

SNOW

for my love

"Like Wordsworth and Dorothy," you said, walking out in the snowy night. Our breath by streetlights and my clogs thickening with snow to skidding, so you laughing caught me. Our fingers laced inside your glove, and stopping at a fork to kiss—the wet cold lips and hot wet tongues. "This isn't like Wordsworth and Dorothy," I said. Across a virgin orchard, still except our puffing breath and crunch, crunch underfoot. Then deer. A little herd fast by—reaching up the trees for fruit—frozen but still fragrant. We stood entranced—a gift. And on the way back home, a father and his small son, "building a Frosty," they called to us. Later, naked before the fire and mulled wine drowsy, we made love slowly, our finger ends and cheeks still chilled, our bellies warm. Your cock inside me thick with love, my body arched, I told you, "Yes," that perfect winter night.

John R. Campbell

DOMESTIC WATERS

1.

I am torn and abolished by this domestic bliss. The bliss itself is so faded and subsumed by the sun that it seems muted, inconsequential—but it is, nonetheless, bliss of the finest sort, as fine as veins, as tendrils. The tenderness I feel towards my daughter and wife, the slow deliberation over banal domestic chores: these congeal like rain in a small depression, and soon a long-hidden seed might sprout, a leaf unfurl over the water like a sail.

Love has settled in, and our household sags. The weight of summer, too, the enormous mass of foliage and vibrant grass. What was the mailwoman singing when she disappeared into her little truck? What was the backyard cook boasting of behind his suffocating smoke? Purplish foothills rim our city like long rosary beads. Crows and vultures commute to the dead with impunity. Our sorry neighbors allow the brush to grow up around their windows and overcome their roof. They know the weight of love as well as we do, and they are bound by love to hide inside nature, to breathe the same musty air their ancestors exhaled.

These details of time and place, by their arbitrary nature, terrify me. The fathomless interactions which form the moment stun me, and I'm involved in that enormous instant like a bee, heavy with pollen, bustling inside a flower. The moment is convoluted and memorable, monumental in scale, unknowable and self-sustaining.

Luckily a river issues from the mountains and runs through our town. The river, like love, either nourishes or sweeps away anything in its course. The results are quick: giant cottonwoods that spangle the air, or pink riffles at dusk. Stoneflies ascending on the summer solstice, each a fluttering lantern. Ermine-colored foam that swirls over the deeper pools, and mergansers trolling their young behind. Could love, as richly endowed as the river, offer us any better? The dress love assumes results from love's passage, and the body that houses love, once recognized, has already moved on to the sea.

This is why I insist that love has abolished me, and why I'm glad. This is why I left my old, troubled family and came west. My household now is vast, and it accommodates everything.

I came west wanting, like a real pioneer. I arrived at the ocean believing I could canter out, like the massive rocks offshore. I wanted fires assembled in mid-air, fed by the purest of oxygens. But when I built my real fires on the beaches, the dense wood burned with an intensity that unnerved me. I saw flaming driftwood figures in a sand pit; I saw something ancient and outside of me. I began to abandon my expectations of the earth. Now when expectation nags, I have the cool basalt to answer nothing; I have the sand so finely ground that it sings underfoot.

I have the open ocean, too. I walk the edge of a realm as strange to me as other planets, and yet the sea is my original world. Have I come so far? Like the stars hidden behind the day sky, prolific life huddles and sways beyond a thin barrier. The ocean houses its own, and excludes all others. Indifferent, exotic, rich beyond belief: no wonder Poseidon, no wonder the white whale. And yet I sense that this hermetic world is part of my household as well—like a cavernous flooded cellar that dwarfs the actual house, akin to the subconscious, but even more unexpected. All the gods, not just the king, reside there easily; the sky gods, bored with heaven, simply empty themselves and fall; the earth gods dissolve and are carried in blue processions to the sea.

I need only follow their trails to arrive home. A crooked spiral, like a speculation, appears as a negative shape in the trees. A cucumber plant curls a thin runner around a twig and climbs. Snail shells wind inward, towards the past, like watch springs in reverse. Everywhere a fine pattern adorns my various household, allowing my attention to fix or to wander. So little is required of me. I need only attend to a few details, to maintain my immediate house with daily love. The rest, the entire world beyond my walls, moves without my knowledge, but it includes me, too—even my pliant will, and my ego hunched in its intimate den.

2.

"The holy is in the heap of dust—it is the heap of dust."
—Kenneth Rexroth

A year ago my lover and I entered the woods behind a huge British Columbia lake, and there was a patch of ground so fecund we were compelled to remove our shoes. Moss, lichens, tiny mushrooms, their cups turned upward to the rain, larger pink mushrooms, warm against all that green—the land quivered underfoot, and water oozed from the spongy earth. When even the ground is alive, it's time to swallow hard, to disappear into the green recesses and to know the life of your own skin, of your own organs throbbing inside. Exactly one year ago we conceived my daughter, who now grins with drowsy love. She's perfectly sensible, a cell we carried back from the wild.

I've spent the last few months descending gradually into a fine depression—by fine I mean sharp and exacting—that grounds me in the carpet of my own ragged house, where flea larvae and certain miniscule beetles roam with impunity. Where dust mites feast on my sloughed-off skin. Where dust itself is forming, each mote, like Keats' urn, a "foster-child of silence and slow time."

In a freer, more romantic time, I could wander to wild places. I could reify my demons in the hot, brown meadows of a ridge, plucking grasshoppers out of the grass and feeling their brittle bodies jump inside my closed hands. I could concentrate on the sheen of the sea below, squinting until my eyes finally closed. But here, behind the white paint and the plaster walls, amid the confined air, I can no longer shelter the abstractions that have defined my pain. Self-pity and remorse become so refined as to disappear. I can't even use them as weapons against myself without engaging in an absurd pantomime.

The freedom of confinement, of a father's responsibility, and of poverty, is this: having no means to seek the exotic, I come to find the mundane crucial. The ordinary, like the Ordinary of the Mass, is nonetheless holy. This domestic life is a return to the junction between the ritual required for religious practice and the ritual required for natural sustenance. Bread is bread here, and is sacred for that.

The summer wanes, cloaked in deep greens, even as the cherry bushes and the rhododendrons climb ever higher at our windows. Depression has a way of muting the light, of keeping my eyes close to my work, and my hands deliberate and slow. I may accomplish only a single, simple task in a long August day. I may not leave the house, or if I do, walking with my wife and baby, the neighborhood seems extravagant to me, as if I'm visiting from a more sober world. The other evening—it was very hot—we saw a stout woman sitting in her picture window, naked, her hair up, a phone tucked under her chin. The plain park down the street was violet and luminescent with shadow, frozen in memory even as it unfolded. The birches and the sycamores were foreign, the firs and maples unusually lush. A steeple on the near horizon caused me to moan. The children playing, even as they mistreated each other, incited a fierce compassion inside me. And looking down, there was my own daughter, sleeping among brilliant patterns in her stroller, her face haunting and so beautiful: the one face in the world that is, thankfully, not my own.

3.

I'm listening to a recording by Miles Davis called *Water Babies*—a minor work in his oeuvre, I suppose, but an important piece of music to me. It's a sort of transitional release from the late sixties, when Miles' second legendary quartet was experimenting with electric colors. The piano textures Herbie Hancock achieves throughout are moody and sure, like the dark Northwest rivers that flow from unfathomable mountains seeking the sea. The dry tone of Wayne Shorter's saxophone is strangely congruent with the liquid flow of his notes, and Miles' phrasing is dense and indispensable, like an understory of ferns. It was while driving a muted dirt road along the Noh River on Washington's Olympic Peninsula, as a matter of fact, listening to this tape, that the music had its maximum impact on me. The music seems incredibly brittle until you realize that it is flowing; like an ice floe in water, the solid and the liquid blur.

Water Babies is water music, if of a very urbane kind. It mixes contraries effortlessly, the way both art and water can. Having listened to *Water Babies* over a number of years and over a number of sometimes very desolate journeys, the music has become ingrained in me, like woodgrain, its liquid grace hardened to an edge. It has become for me one model of what art can achieve. Especially in its stiller moments (where sound pools), there is no past, no future to speak of: there is only the present, swelling like rain. The swelling abounds in emptiness, or perhaps it's the other way around. Phillip Whalen says, "The emptiness is the thing we're full of, and everything that you're seeing here is empty. Literally the word is *shunya*, something that's swollen up; it's not, as often translated, 'void.'"

The landscape of the western United States is especially like that, full to the brim with emptiness. The emptiness is quite graphic here, whether you're in a Northwest rainforest, your eyes accustomed to the gloom, or dazzled by Great Basin distances, your eyes coming to roost on a lizard's nondescript back. Moving across this west occupies much of my time, but I'm only travelling in order to come to rest. The length and quality of the travel, the intervals between images, the changes in the landscape as I pass through: all these affect my experience of arrival, so that in a sense, the journey is the destination. And returning home, the quiet domestic life after the odyssey is formed of the tumult and motion of the trip. That's how I see melody, and improvisation too. The notes exist in order to articulate the spaces between. The song exists for the moment the song is over, the moment coaxed into the future with the promise of song.

4.

My lover and I arrived in October in Northern California, in our twenties, almost penniless. We were dazed from days of driving west, days of witnessing corn maidens skipping across the highways, of tasting thick new snow in the Absaroka Range, of listening to the rattling and failing cylinders in the truck which held everything we owned. We answered an ad for hands on a crumbling Appaloosa ranch with the too-cute name of Acorn Acres, and were hired on. No pay: only room and board in exchange for the daily feedings, the mucking out of the stalls. We lived in an old trailer, a Pontiac Chief, the type they pulled behind cars in the fifties. Because of its shape and aluminum walls, we called it "the canned ham." Because of its size, maybe we should have referred to canned sardines instead.

We had wanted transience; we had wanted America; we had wanted the West. That's exactly what we got. An old school bus, half converted to a motorhome and lacking a transmission, was parked directly in front of our only sizable window. The ranch owners couldn't understand our insistence it be moved. All around the ranch the California hills sulked in their drab brown summer grasses. They threatened in a vague way to burn; but mostly they were listless, animated only by occasional grasshoppers. We had not yet learned to call them golden.

Even the Appaloosas on the ranch were slow and decrepit, with the exception of a few who were going feral. Rarely ridden, these became unruly: one clipped my lover from her blind-side and split open her mouth. We confronted the unpredictable horses with all the city aplomb we could muster, but we were out of our element. So we preferred the company of the more docile Appaloosas, whom we combed, whom we spoke to in low, reassuring tones.

Soon the rains arrived. The ranch-owners seemed perturbed. But over a few days, we watched the hills transform: they became a miraculous, vital green; they glowed from within. A creek began to run outside our trailer door, the stones suddenly gleaming. Deer emerged from the surrounding oaks and fed in the pastures. As they bowed their heads to the new grass, all I could feel was gratitude. I would spend my days hiking through the hills, gathering deer skulls from the creek beds, learning the birds: flickers, orange-shafted and startling, and scrub jays, blue and grey like the shifting winter skies. I saw larks roosting on the ground, and red-tailed hawks filtering the sun. The oaks dripped with lichen and rain, and I wandered among them like an innocent among elders—foolish, happy, never overtly regarded, but never allowed to stray.

There is a moment when the very landscape opens like palms on all sides, offering friendship. Our poverty was real, and our situation was anything but idyllic, but for a time the hills let their waters down in front of my astonished face, and I lived in those waters as easily and unselfconsciously as an ouzel in a creek. For a time. But long enough to allow my first artistic expression, and long enough to let me pull that instant into the present, through memory, through the flow and continuum of my life.

5.

I live in another hollow now, in Oregon, among other giving ridges. My lover and I have married and have a baby girl. Living in a literal depression through the dark winters has affected us somehow: it's deepened the waters, and stirred something undefinable that rises up.

Once while fishing the Umpqua River, I saw what can only be described as a feeding frenzy. Among trout. I was jigging a wooly-worm fly at the base of a whitewater stretch where the water was deep and oxygenated, and rock shelves lined both sides of the stream. Suddenly I saw one quick rise after another, as the fish surged up for the fly. Their bodies appeared dark at first, but as they lunged and twisted away, they flashed silver at the water's surface in streaks and crescents like a hundred glimpses of the moon.

Some of the fish missed their mark. Others hit and spit. A dozen or more, over a half-hour's time, were hooked, admired, released. Three, pan-sized, came home for dinner. Even in the skillet, the trout exuded grace. They entered our house and our bodies with dignity, after a show of skill I'll never achieve.

If I were to rise from sleep with such deftness and glint, I'd be a god, I'd be an innocent. I'd be like I once was, an unborn thrusting in the womb. As it is, I'm lucky enough to be infused with water. It passes through me like a diffuse river; it comprises most of my cells.

My family, too, is fluid, changing with each season, in relationship with each other, attuned. Our baby, drawn and amazed by water, points and cries out whenever we trace the swollen creek south of the house. All that soul out there: the rivers, the mountain lakes, the ocean hurling weather to coat us in rain. Wearing rain, or just-melted snow, we meander or rush home, hopefully by a most circuitous route. We realize, after wearing water for all these years, that we are nothing more than what we wear. The water we contain joins the water that contains us and there we are, at an exact boundary, at the thinnest of walls, humming our osmotic song.

6.

At the dunes this autumn Sunday, my wife and I sit in the mist, while our baby naps. We're snug among snub-needled pines, listening to the surf, and to two ravens, their trickster calls.

We're talking of our distant families drinking and watching the football games. We miss them, though we don't exactly crave their company, and this mix of emotions puzzles us. The huckleberries that glow under low skies, and the few animals, who ignore us, can't cheer us. The wasp with her pumpkin-orange abdomen, intent on burrowing, can't cheer us either: she's digging in to lay and die.

Yet this is where we live. My wife bends down to show me the seasons in a grassblade: an almost fluorescent green base, a deep green that tapers to yellow, and finally a simple gray-white.

She tells me about praying as a child, the listing she'd do before bed each night, and she mentions her confusion: was she simply naming her family members for a forgetful god? Or was she actually invoking *their* powers through her prayer?

My own concept of prayer has to do with desperation: *Genius, god,* I say, *your people are rushing towards you, arms raised. Where they stop to kneel in despair, the clay rises up and takes the shape of their bodies.*

Then I can recognize the sea as my own pain, distended to the point of transparency. The empty horizon, so long it curves, expands my vision. The god I long for becomes as invisible to me as the eyes I see right through. My future child tripping in the tidepools, glimpsing the anenomies and the brittle stars: she will formulate her own list of blessings.

D. M. Wallace

SIEVES

The sun is a bird that rises
on its very own schedule.
Immediate tasks are at hand
and my hands take flight,
bean picking, berry washing,
knocking slugs off the deck.
The hands that climb trees
are sticky with sap. One
drop of maple syrup draws
a circle of ants. There are
bee stings to be washed,
a thorn to be drawn out
backward from the wound.
Insects and simple sugars,
dirt, a fingernail, our bodies
become sieves for everything
that matters, matter itself
bleeding, mutable, beautiful.
Wildflower seeds scatter
on hot wind. Even the clouds
have somewhere to go,
disappearing deliberately
toward the south. Birds
rule the air, absolutely.

EROS

Not sleeping, but smoking Camels
at the kitchen table while
everyone else sleeps.
Not sleeping when I should
because I should. Baking cookies
at midnight, because at midnight
the kitchen is all mine,
and the smell of baking chocolate
is just for me. Not sleeping,
like slipping out the door
in the middle of the night
when I was thirteen because snow
coated everything, made the night
as light as a gray winter day.
Walked alone. Scared myself,
invented crisp conversations between
people who are all me, now, not
sleeping, but remembering sleep, making
love to my first boyfriend, like
I made a god out of the painter
who smudged my electric blue leggings
with white. Not sleeping, but dreaming,
swirling sea water in a tea cup.
Painting a small table and chairs blue.
Painting a mirror's back black.
Lighting white candles, almond incense,
the gas oven, dousing everything with
light, heat, sweet and heavy odor.
Burning my hand on the stove.
Washing black panties in cold water.
Not sleeping, but constructing metaphors
for sleep. Eating cookie dough, but
not the cookies. Making patterns
for children's pants out of newspaper.
Cropping photographs. Writing letters
to Congress. Washing dishes quietly.
Not sleeping, but wanting to.
Pouring sour milk down the drain.
Putting the cat on top of the refrigerator.
Listening to my boys talking in their sleep.

Folding the clean, warm clothes, avoiding
the hot snaps. Not sleeping, but seeing
the backyard in Idaho, the fence
dad built when I was sixteen, that
same summer mowing the front lawn
under the street light, entranced
by the slice of the push mower's blade
dicing the red and orange nasturtiums.
Falling off the steps after my first,
real kiss. Paul Hernandez.
Not sleeping, but remembering every bed
I've ever slept in. The over-soft,
the hard floors, sleeping bags, men
with braided hair, women with large
breasts. Sleeping on the Interstate,
sandwiched between children in disposable
diapers. Sleeping, as a woman, with mom
while dad negotiated with the CWA in
Denver, her snore keeping me awake,
amused. Not sleeping, but waiting,
trying to forget the wind that ripped
over my childhood. Waiting to grow up.
Tracking my stoned footprints through
the City of Rocks, hitchhiking under stars
unafraid, down roads lined with mile markers,
rusted railroad ties and gophers.
Walking toward the faint sound
of country music. Not sleeping,
but looking months ahead, planning
my private life, my great escape
to Cape Cod, the winter sun setting
far off in mist, my bearded lover
with a fishing pole and a grin,
drinking vodka, smelling of oil paint.
Not sleeping, but wanting sex,
an unfamiliar tongue, Eros incarnate,
the taste of red meat and red wine.
Listening for the foghorn at
Provincetown, Massachusetts,
and hearing it in Eugene, Oregon.
Listening for the wind that rages
off the Atlantic, but hearing only

the rain falling steadily into the
Willamette Valley, running in rivulets
down my roof. Sending my lover a towel
for Christmas. Not sleeping, but
needing sleep. Blowing out candles that
leave the smell of someone's birthday
in the air. Telling my husband that
I love him, and meaning it. Whispering
into a sleeping ear. Sleeping, but
not sleeping. Believing I have become
the tooth fairy, I am pushing the
calcified fragments into potted plants.
Hiding cookies from the kids.
Hiding new packs of cigarettes
from my husband. Brushing dirt
and twigs from my cat's fur.
Drinking cold milk from the carton.
Leaving the heat on High.
Folding crisp twenty-dollar bills
into an old honey jar.
Sitting in the dark, lying down
in the light. Sleeping, but forgetting
how to sleep. Forgetting nothing.

SEX MACHINE

Chug, chug, thunk, now
the machine comes to life.
All it wants to do is wring
the scalding waters from
my twisted bedsheets but

it gets unbalanced, loud.
I readjust and lie over it,
the sheer weight of my body
the only thing keeping it
in the room. My belly gets

warm against the enameled
lid, so smooth, coming up
to speed on the spin cycle,
topping off and whirring, purring
beneath my premenstrual mound.

I go with it, trusting
this helpful tool to work
another miracle. I go away,
into the rhythmic squeak-bump
of gyrating metal and me.

Wee, making whoopie and washing
bedding at the same time, a gal
could get used to this, giving
sultry and steamy praise to the
god of mechanic, phallic agitation.

I give into this technological advance
as the ungainly lover gives himself
to his own hand, my hand, and the
clumsy machine taking me home.

Dorianne Laux

KISSING

They are kissing, on a park bench,
on the edge of an old bed, in a doorway
or on the floor of a church. Kissing
as the streets fill with balloons
or soldiers, locusts or confetti, water
or fire or dust. Kissing down through
the centuries under sun or stars, a dead tree,
an umbrella, amid derelicts. Kissing
as Christ carries his cross, as Gandhi
sings his speeches, as a bullet
careens through the air toward a child's
good heart. They are kissing,
long, deep, spacious kisses, exploring
the silence of the tongue, the mute
rungs of the upper palate, hungry
for the living flesh. They are still
kissing when the cars crash and the bombs
drop, when the babies are born crying
into the white air, when Mozart bends
to his bowl of soup and Stalin
bends to his garden. They are kissing
to begin the world again. Nothing
can stop them. They kiss until their lips
swell, their thick tongues quickening
to the budded touch, licking up
the sweet juices. I want to believe
they are kissing to save the world,
but they're not. All they know
is this press and need, these two-legged
beasts, their faces like roses crushed
together and opening, they are covering
their teeth, they are doing what they have to do
to survive the worst, they are sealing
the hard words in, they are dying
for our sins. In a broken world they are
practicing this simple and singular act
to perfection. They are holding
onto each other. They are kissing.

Jeff Walt

MORE THAN SPRING

My cat reacts to spring with great alacrity.
She does a figure eight between my legs

as if just born into the present
after a winter of warm blankets and sleep—

all that she adores. I know her
as anyone knows the one thing they love

in this world. She is not like me:
The clear, white sky does not satisfy her

She expects more than this.
More than spring and morning; wants

more than the day after
and the soul they say she lacks.

She doesn't understand the words
disease or *death* or *AZT*.

She wants to feel the word *love*
glide down her spine and coil her tail

in one flat, even stroke.
I listen to her small heart.

I think of all she doesn't know.

AFTERNOON ON THE STOOP

Birds quarrel in the thicket
after a sudden storm
that lasted only minutes.
The pink blossoms were torn
from trees and tossed violently
into the streets. The warm,
setting sun smells of nectar
drifting from the apple orchard.

All this
while someone that loves me
hums behind the screen door in the kitchen.
Broken branches lie in the street.
The day turns its back to me.
The moon and stars light the East.

Emily Robertson

FOR THE BROTHER OF CORTEZ

Love could be like this/ soft brazilian music/ the smell of cinnamon/ ginger/ rose burnin'/ where sweat mixes with steam/ raining from the ceiling/ a house/ a room/ a shelter/ built of palm leaves/ a floor of sand or dust/ love could be like this/ curried chicken/ rice cooked with peanut sauce/ and coconut milk/ flowin' from my lips/ where you offered it to a velvet tongue/ and eyes that see only one other body in the darkness/ know only one body external to their own/ a body well known/ but eternally new/ softly/ evolving/ under each touch/ into something strange/ something exotic/ something jungle/ alive with animals/ that stay quiet in the night/ but breathe/ these heartbeats/ under yellow feathers/ and scaled skin/ the jungle is alive with unseen eyes/ love could be like this/ a pool of still water/ where the river no longer flows/ but so alive/ tiny organisms are starting a new world here/ Love/ could be like this

LOVE TELLS HER STORY

Here is my candlelit night/
  shadows dancin'/ incense burnin'/
in your hands.
  Take me back to the lands my flower
first grew in/

You didn't /
  understand/
  a paved world is not
        fertile/
to me/
i grow through the cracks
  what you assumed wuz a weed/
Becuz my roots continually/
                force/

  REBIRTH/

        i surprised you/
in the springtime a bold blossom fanning from a sidewalk
        crack/
You thought i was weak/
  possessing the characteristics
  of any ordinary/practiced

  slut/

just becuz i understand the presence of a woman's body
        will add life to any party/
will be the candle lighted
        and incense burning/
a woman will be/
  the shadows dancin'

This power i know/ this power i hold/
  i don't believe in pavement/
  i don't believe in cement
i like/ earth/ soil/ the feel of minerals flooding my skin as i grow/

my roots/

continually/ force/ REBIRTH

i grow stronger/ each passing of the sun
my blossom that grows through a crack
in the sidewalk

will one day
turn that crack into a fault/
will one day/
split the cement shell open/

My roots/
continually/
force/

REBIRTH

i am essential/
in the freeing of the earth.

Willa Schneberg

BEDDING DOWN

Yippie!, it's time for the egg cups
to lie on their sides,
the knives flat on their backs,
the cards neat in their decks
in the kitchen drawer,
for the window's big eye
to flirt with the moon and for
the two who undress in that room
not to fight or bemoan what
they didn't do today
or need to do tomorrow,
but to climb nude as olives
between flannel sheets
and fit together like a teaspoon
and a tablespoon measuring nothing.

THE BELLS OF SAINT BAVO SING SCAT

Anticipating the lovers
who will soon be voices with bodies again,
the comforter on the bed fills with light
the color of the sky when day puts up her feet and
slips on royal blue slippers.

Outside their window
the man on the roof dangles a dancing bear
or a baby grand or whatever
the lovers want to unhook and haul inside.

Finally, their bodies are fields
of yellow tulips fringed purple slowly opening their fists,
the bells of St. Bavo singing scat,
fire-breathing dragons barreling out of children's books
to race through the streets of Haarlem.

Belts fathers used for beatings stay in the loops of their pants.
Charred bodies resurrect themselves noticing
a faint smell of smoke in their sleek hair or
the tweed of their jackets, while lovers
who parted without declaring their love
feverishly lick stamps on envelopes of yellowed love letters
or scratch at the blood red wax seals.

Elizabeth Sinclaire

from GRAND CANYON JOURNAL

June 5, 1993

At the Las Vegas Airport

Beep beep.
Perky electric cars pass
through the voluminous halls,
stop to pick up/drop off
the old, the infirm, the tired and the lazy.
Their motors hum, speed up—slow down—stop,
as they slide from one gate to another.
I'm fighting a headache, in three hours
a Twin Otter to the South Rim.
Meanwhile, the ring of the slots,
the second hand smoke. Through windows
I see dark thunderclouds surrounding
Las Vegas like a fence of open gray hands.

Constant plane dreams, I hate to fly,
but I don't see my body sliced
by the razors of torn fuselage,
a disarticulated elbow and forearm
dangling from a cactus. No,
when I close my eyes I see a person
lying on the sand, two gashes above
the right eye. Tomorrow, I'll climb down
to Phantom Ranch and the rafts. Never flown
in a small plane in a storm, rising and falling
like an angel in a nightmare amusement park ride
or like an angel tumbling through purgatory,
although sometimes the hawks I watch are lifted
by the current, drift upwards as if toward God.
Hello fear, paranoia, premonition, change,
are these the last few hours of my life,
and what have I to say? A small thing.
Fear. I've been scared very often.

June 8, 1993

I. Running the Colorado

On the river, something happens to my head.
Key opened, seal broken, the metal strip peeled back,
the cap no longer air tight, I begin to let in the spirits.
Rocks rise up in the current and dance before the raft.
They invite the water over them, light flickering
like stars, like swarms of bright bugs rising. Red rocks
clicking together, dancing, holding out their hands to me, their hearts.
Thick blood of river runs through and over them, curling and rising
up, curling and breaking. The rocks rise over the boat in waves.
The rafts run on invisible water over this landscape of rocks, pulled
by the tight fist of the current.

II. Photons

I want to tell you how the sun
would slice through me if it could,
how stones click together deep under the raft,
how I hear a fly panic, trapped beneath a stack
of orange life jackets.

Mother, I float down the River Styx,
what part of my life has grown obsolete?
Airplanes buzz beyond these cliffs,
through the nightmare we live in.

Still my heart squishes its squeaky
blood, and lungs steadily pump the air in,
the air out. I can eddy where a fresh creek
enters, curl away for a moment in the happy,
empty air.

III. In the Canyon

Sometimes what possesses you is taken from your hands,
and you stand there breathing and confused.
As I enter this body all time stops, gives way

to rush of water, the mute ring of the sun.
Passing through the layered escarpments
I have no words. At sunset, flies flit
through shadows I do not see. At night
I lie listening to cool river blood, and oars
continually swishing in the current.

IV. Roll Me

All I can offer is this small life,
can I wrap it around your shoulders like a shawl,
and sing in the movement of this instrument called my body.
I am weaving praise, goddess, weaving it into spine and rock,
into leather and my heart. Bring me back to you, bring me back.
My sleeping bag is full of sand, shooting stars
I've gathered in sheaths. My mouth is full and clumsy.
Bring me back, mother, roll me in the current of your arms.

V. Bugs

This night the gnats batter my nose
and the stars are scars in the sky.
Black river flows high through the galaxy,
scatters light back here among planets I'll never know:
Agave, Century Plant, Prickly Pear, and Saltcedar.

VI. Poetry

We are all the dust of stars,
scattered across this planet.
The clear page is illusion,
dancing before these cliffs like heat.

Hannah Wilson

DOUBLING

Each time I reach for the red saucepan
that hangs over the stove and holds
just one cup of water to a half of oatmeal,
I think of Pat who bought it in London,
mailed it here to me in Oregon.
Like the continents blackened on its bottom,
we too drift.
                                        I can name
an alphabet of girls and women
who held one end of the rope
bridges we jumped over and crossed
together until one needed both hands
to hold a job, change a diaper,
                                        steer and shift.
Untied by blood or ceremony, we slipped
into separations once unthinkable
                                        and discovered
no one is interchangeable. Friendship
folds slowly on itself like thick batter—
a secret wildness proffered, accepted
in kind; a depth sounded,
resounded in ourselves—and we pour it
into cups, no two shapes exactly alike.

Tonight in my Emerald Street kitchen
I twist open a jar of coriander,
it whiffs me back across Galata Bridge,
it's April, I stroll through the Spice Bazaar
alongside Miriam, missing Jane, wishing
I could step, like a Colossus, from Istanbul
to home, and back again,

or be like Crow of medicine story,
in two places at one time.
Now I know
why she pecked at her shadow till it woke
and devoured her—this hunger for inseparability.
When girls, we swap blouses and skirts; grown,
we become each other's stories,
lengthened extensions of selves
seeking nourishment from twinned increase.

MAKE OF YOURSELF A LIGHT

after a line of Mary Oliver's

The poem says the Buddha said
Make of yourself a light..

That is all. I am relieved
of the need to be Good,

to be Wise, to be Other.
All I need do is walk ahead

so my children can see
into the dark.

Laure-Anne Bosselaar

INVENTORY

Thanksgiving today. Soaked with sleet.
No sun for six days—six is the Devil's number.
I have looked through this window,
at these American skies for two times six years.
My wall is covered with photographs of distant friends.

This is my second garden. The first one blossomed in Belgium.
Where there is no Thanksgiving. Where my father is buried.
Where I was raised and raped and worked. Where I had five lovers,
but loved only one. Where I gave birth to three children.
A blond son, a dead daughter, a blond daughter.

Two larches grew in my first garden.
Because of North sea winds and how they stood, they fused
into one trunk. It wounded them at first, that rubbing together—
the frailest larch losing sap for months, a lucid sap that glued them
to each other. I saw it as an omen for my life.

I give thanks for the lowlands in Belgium.
For Flanders, her canals and taciturn skies. For the tall ships
on the river Scheldt. For coal pyramids in Wallonia.
For the color of hop, and the hop-pickers' songs.
For Antwerp's whores who woo sailors in six different tongues.

Six is the Devil's number. My grandfather and a farmer
killed six German soldiers and buried them in a Flemish moor.
I can no longer give thanks for that: I ask mercy.
Before I die, I'll plant a larch by the moor—*miserere* —
the soldiers' mothers will never know it was done.

I prayed six years for the death of my Jew-hating father,
I ask mercy for that also: it's Thanksgiving today.
I give thanks for my son and daughter, for the man I love
who taught me to speak a new language,
for this garden's weeds and sleet.

Before I left for this vast continent,
I stole a pebble from the river Scheldt,
an inch of barbed wire from a Concentration Camp near Antwerp,
a leaf from the chestnut tree behind Apollinaire's grave,
but no weed, not a seed of it, growing from my father's ashes.

In Belgium, the day is almost over.
Soon, a new century will make History: *miserere.*
Four larches grow in my garden, one for my son, one for my daughter —
and far from a moor in Flanders, the other two
fuse here: in America. In America.

Yvonne Vowels

SURRENDERING INTO DESTINY

[A codependent] is afraid of rejection or retribution every time she says I want, I feel, or I think.

—Charlotte Kasl,
Women, Sex, and Addiction

[A]dolescent and adult women silence themselves or are silenced in relationships rather than risk open conflict and disagreement that might lead to isolation or to violence.

—Carol Gilligan,
Meeting at the Crossroads

In a world where a man's word is his honor, and where female human beings have been both silenced and dishonored for millennia, the word of a women seems a fragile thing. But to break silence is an act of audacity, with enormous implications. And, given all the means by which silence is reinforced again and again, to break and re-break it one's whole life long, in newer and different ways, is an honorable and gratifying task, a humbling sort of hubris.

—Robin Morgan,
The Word of a Woman

The above words of subversive, feminist wisdom hang at eye level from the window sill behind my desk. Every day as I sit down to write—to commit audacious acts—I inhale these words into myself. Taken as a whole, they remind me that my otherness/difference is a source not of perversity or evil but of subjugated knowledge. More importantly, they remind me that though there are real reasons to be afraid, such fear is not incompatible with action. No matter how frightened I might sometimes feel, I must not compromise my own unique perspective on truth. I knew these things as a young girl but had forgotten. Now, daily, I am remembering. As a consequence, I am reclaiming the courage to speak the unspeakable.

This breaking of silence accomplishes a breaking down of both false connections and false dichotomies, allowing for the recognition and honoring of authentic relationships, such as the one between personal experience and political action—as expressed in the radical feminist adage: the personal is political. In keeping with this feminist insight, the following story of how I finally learned to embrace my fear and surrender into destiny interweaves personal and political elements.

I begin with a reliving of the moment I first became acutely aware, as an adult, of the danger of "being different" and of allowing the knowledge derived from encountering such difference to surface—of speaking in a"different voice"[1] without equivocation or apology. The year was 1985. I was a graduate teaching "fellow" in the Religious Studies Department at the University of Oregon, and though I had previously held positions of considerable *responsibility*, this was my first experience in a position of any real *authority*.

As I stood before the large, undergraduate class, about to commit what I considered an act of heroic self-assertion, in the form of a feminist critique of certain patriarchal religious themes, I saw that while a few of the students seemed open and attentive, most were shielded behind attitudes of indifference and/or boredom. I knew that what I was about to say would be provocative, even shocking to some, and was momentarily overcome with a whole range of powerful, conflicting emotions.

My inner turmoil took on a visual, metaphorical life of its own as I struggled to compose myself. Pictures flashed in slow motion on the projection screen in my mind while students continued to shuffle in and take their seats. My whole life crowded in upon me in those moments. The first image I saw was of a wrathful Yahweh hovering in a cloud bank above me, hurling lightning bolts at my upper torso. Second, I saw myself being burned at the stake while Inquisitors fed the flames. Next, I saw my father standing over my mother, his face contorted in rage, his hands tight around her throat, choking her. Finally, as I struggled to open my mouth and speak, I saw myself as a fire-breathing dragon-woman, capable of incinerating anyone or anything in my path. I shook; I perspired; my throat constricted; my hands grew cold and clammy; I felt light-headed and sick to my stomach. I wanted nothing more in those moments than to go home, lock the door to my apartment, and never come out. I wanted to disintegrate or disappear—to somehow relieve myself of the burden of my otherness, of knowing what I knew and felt compelled, despite paralyzing fear, to communicate.

In retrospect, I now understand that in those brief moments, I was caught on the horns of what I have come to call the dilemma of

---

[1] The phrase "in a different voice" is in reference to Carol Gilligan's groundbreaking book *In a Different Voice* (Cambridge: Harvard University Press, 1982), in which Gilligan argues that women tend to speak with a voice of responsibility and care for others while men tend to speak with a voice emphasizing individual rights.

self-assertion vs. self-sacrifice; twisted into knots by internalized contradictions and gross distortions stemming from the false, patriarchal dichotomy between agency and passivity, as well as from the more general tendency to reify and hierarchalize difference. As a consequence of my own unique, and yet all too common, life experiences as a white, working-class, female Baby Boomer, raised in a dysfunctional U.S. home, I had internalized certain messages about self-assertion and self-sacrifice that were now rising up to haunt and disorient me.

Generally speaking, I had learned that self-assertion was frequently distorted into an expression of male privilege, taking the form of unpredictable, explosive outbursts and/or acts of contemptuous superiority, directed at women and children for the purpose of control and domination. I had seen that it was often dangerous to tell the truth about one's experience, and that legitimate anger on the part of women and children was usually dismissed, invalidated, and/or punished. I had learned that self-sacrifice was typically distorted into an expression of subordination with crippling effects, especially for women, robbing us of authentic selfhood. I had witnessed women denying their own needs, in the never-ending service to their children and their anger, out of fear of abandonment or retaliation, and then watched as the consequent bitterness and resentment seeped out in subtle and not so subtle ways, ironically poisoning their relationships with those for whom they had sacrificed the most. I had learned that often when men make sacrifices in their role as providers, they assume that such sacrifice gives them license to dictate how those who are financially dependent upon them will think, feel, and behave. Tragically, I had also learned that working-class men, caught in the contradiction between their oppressed status as members of the working class and their privileged, heroic status as men, will sometimes implode under the pressure, sacrificing their very lives. By way of further explanation, I will elaborate on the images that confronted me that day.

My Father Choking My Mother and Me as a Fire-breathing Dragon-woman

The images of my father choking my mother and of me as a fire-breathing dragon-woman are closely related. The former encapsulates my relationship with my father and the dynamic between my parents. The latter represents my relationship with my mother, as understood, of course, in the context of male-domination.

My parents met at a gas-station in Greenville, Michigan, in 1952. My father, having recently returned from Germany where he was stationed during the Korean War, was pumping gas when my mother pulled in for a fill-up on her way to work in a local factory. The parallels in their lives were quite remarkable, so it was not surprising that they were drawn to one another. For example, both were from fourth generation Irish/American, working-class families who had settled in the Midwest; both had violent, alcoholic fathers and cowering, codependent mothers; and both were approximately twelve years old when their parents divorced due to their fathers' increasingly violent, alcoholic behavior.

Within a short time my parents were married (Dad was twenty-four; Mom was nineteen), with five children, my twin sister and I and three younger siblings, born in rapid succession. Dad, who worked as a mechanic and a taxi-driver by day and attended Business College at night, was rarely home in those early days. Mom, as was true of many U.S. women in the 1950s, had her hands full with constant childbirth, childrearing, and homemaking responsibilities. Much later I learned that she had intended to have only two children, but, with increasing resentment, exhaustion, and bitterness, had "given in" to my father's pressure to "give him sons."

In 1959, after my youngest sister was born, our family set out on the quintessential American adventure. In the dead of a Michigan winter, with snow piled high on the ground, we left the frozen Midwest for sunny Southern California in pursuit of "the good life," or, at least, a better one: warmer weather; lucrative employment opportunities; and distance from extended-family dysfunction. It was an upscale, abbreviated, 1950s version of *The Grapes of Wrath*: five kids sleeping/playing/eating/fighting on a matress in the back of an old green stationwagon as we made our way relentlessly Westward with a U-Haul trailer in tow. Since there was no money in the budget for staying in motels, our weary but hopeful parents alternately drove and slept in the front seat.

Shortly after arriving in Los Angeles, my father did, in fact, manage to find a better paying job, and, consequently, was home more in the evenings and on the weekends than previously. Even so, his presence was a confusing and heartbreaking kind of absence. He seemed to suffer from the type of low-level, chronic depression common among "maintenance alcoholics," spending most of his offwork hours lying on the couch nursing a beer or a bottle of whiskey, smoking cigarettes, and watching televised sports. Unfortunately, what little energy and attention my father had for parenting was directed toward my brother in the form of various rituals of indoctrination into manhood.

On the surface, I worshipped my father and longed for his attention and validation. Some of this longing was transferred to the ruggedly handsome, and, yet, completely remote and unattainable, male protagonists of three television shows which were popular in the early to mid 1960s: *The Fugitive, Perry Mason,* and *Gunsmoke.* I watched these programs faithfully, pining away for their vulnerable yet stoic stars—all of whom looked and behaved remarkably like my father. Under the surface of such transference and denial, however, I felt deeply hurt and angry with my father for his betrayal and emotional abandonment of me and my three sisters for the apparent reason that we were not boys.

My mother was more energetic than my father, but the strain of four pregnancies in rapid succession (including the unexpected birth of premature twins, after which she lapsed into a coma for three days), in combination with the stresses and strains of an unhappy and abusive marriage, had taken its toll and soon after the move to California her decaying teeth were extracted and she was fitted with false ones. She was twenty-five years old. I can still see my mother in my mind's eye the day she came home from the dentist's office, after having all of her teeth pulled. As she curled up on the couch like a wounded animal, I felt her suffering in my bones, in the pit of my stomach, in the heaviness around my heart. I tell this story reluctantly, not to embarrass my mother but to convey something of the extent of her self-sacrifice and its effect on me. In my child's memory, my mother is perpetually cleaning, cooking, chauffeuring, and sewing school clothes for us—taking care of everyone but herself.

Perhaps the most noteworthy thing about my mother in those early years, and certainly, the most relevant to this discussion of self-assertion, however, was her fiery temper. During those times when the wounds of unresolved hurt from her own difficult childhood were laid open again by some similar event in the present, or when protecting her children from some perceived threat, my mother seemed capable of incinerating everything in her path. She was the fire-breathing dragon-woman of my childhood. Even so, there was an aspect of her anger that always struck me as healthy, no matter how frightening. In some elusive way, my mother seemed most real, most herself, when she was angry. The fact that there was something subversive about her anger, something "not nice" but necessary, was not lost on me. Somehow, I knew my mother was fighting for her life in the only way she knew how. Secretly, I rooted for her anger to triumph over her passivity and despair.

Unfortunately, in most areas of my mother's life, she had forgotten herself and thus, could not be an ally for me and my three sisters.

Whatever anger I felt toward my mother as a child stemmed primarily from the fact that, like my father, she valued her son more than she valued her daughters. (This was not merely my perception, but a fact which has since been confirmed in the course of family therapy.) For my passionate resistance to this state of affairs, I was labelled "selfish," "bossy, "strong-willed," "smart-mouthed," and "not nice." These assaults were confusing and withering to my spirit.

At the same time, I had a great deal of empathy and compassion for both my parents and felt responsible for their suffering. So much so, in fact, that I often wished that I could disappear to relieve them of the burden I felt I was to them. At the age of seven I had a recurring nightmare in which I returned home from school to discover that my siblings and I had been abandoned, whereupon I calmly took control of the situation, leading "the kids" to an orphanage, conveniently located at the end of the block. After making arrangements for them to be cared for, and, with a feeling of guilty relief, I then ran away.

As the oldest child (though only five minutes older than my twin sister, I was raised as the oldest), I absorbed the dynamics of my parents relationship without benefit of a sibling "buffer zone." I understood on an unconscious level that my father had a great need to control my mother and that she was terrified of him. Ultimately, my father was prepared to enforce his rule with physical violence, if necessary, but my mother was so cowed by him, and so used to living her life "on egg shells," that dad rarely had to follow through on his implied threats.

The dynamics of my parents relationship began to shift precariously when my mother took a job as a cashier in a convenience store in 1965. I was eleven years old at the time—old enough to notice that change was in the air. As a result of the confidence gained from her work experience, my mother began challenging my father's authority in very modest ways, for example, by wearing lipstick to the grocery store, or shopping by herself without at least one of her children along as a chaperone. Her resistance, which had always been underground, began to surface more and more frequently, until one night after dinner a fight erupted between the two of them, culminating in my father's attempt to choke my mother into submission, while my siblings and I watched in horror and pleaded with him to stop.

That night I secretly wished that my father would die. There seemed no other solution. Approximately one month later, much to my numb and guilty disbelief, he did, in fact, die suddenly of a massive brain hemorrhage. He was thirty-eight years old; I was thirteen. According to family legend, my father miraculously regained consciousness in the ambulance on the way to the hospital long enough to make the following plea to the attendant: "Please don't let me die; I have five kids at home to support."

After relocating the family to Michigan in order to avail herself of extended-family support, Mom got a job as a secretary and began attending a local Community College part-time. For a couple of years she admittedly contemplated suicide whenever she had a spare moment and cried herself to sleep every night, but gradually she began to reclaim her own latent strength and wisdom. Two poignant and empowering images stand out in my memory of my mother during that time: in the first she is bent over the kitchen table intently writing a term paper in long-hand; in the second she is speaking with great passion and courage to a "death and dying" class at the local Community College about the experience of being widowed at the age of thirty-three, with five young children and almost no experience in the paid labor force.

As the shock of my father's death began to subside and I was able to grieve, though only very superficially in those early years, I began to notice new feelings of freedom and relief, mixed with guilt and great longing for the father I would never know. With Mom busy working and finding herself, we kids (all teenagers at the same time!) were left to fend for ourselves, more or less. I went through the motions of high school but found my greatest comfort and distraction in extra-curricular activities, namely, girls' sports; art projects; a part-time job; Friday night slumber parties; and boys—not necessarily in that order.

Ten years later, after a brief marriage at nineteen to my high-school sweetheart, a truck driver who had introduced me to the great escape of drug abuse, I bottomed-out and began to face the nothingness at the center of my life. A vivid nightmare, in which I encountered my father as a rotting zombie, resembling something out of *The Night of the Living Dead*, broke through my numbness and denial and gave me the impetus to grieve in earnest. In the process, I was able to begin to see my father more realistically and to reclaim lost pieces of myself. It was then, after moving to the Northwest at the age of twenty-three, that I made the bold decision, given my class background and gender, to go to college.

Yahweh Hurling Lightning Bolts at Me

The image of a wrathful Yahweh poised in a cloud bank hurling lightning bolts at my upper torso represents my exposure to popular, mainstream Christianity as a child. The first time I remember really struggling with monotheistic concerns I was five years old and the family dog had just been killed in a close encounter with an automobile. I needed to understand why God would allow such a thing to happen, but had very little information to go on. I knew, of course, that God was a man. From what I could gather He seemed a lot like an elderly version of my dad: imposing, unpredictable, remote, unreachable, authoritarian, mysterious, awe-inspiring, controlling, and handsome. Oddly enough, in the dark of my room at night as I prayed for Blondie, the family dog, to go to Heaven, God was also pretty much interchangeable with the Bogey Man whom I was certain lived in the shadows beneath my bed.

Obviously, I felt no great affinity for the God of my childhood understanding. In this regard, I got no guidance from either of my parents. For reasons stemming in part from the history of Protestant/Catholic strife in Ireland—a history which had left scars down through the generations of Irish immigrants to the U.S.—my mother was openly hostile toward God/religion, and Dad seemed too tired and defeated to care. My only memories of religious involvement as a child are of attending Bible study classes, where I learned about Jesus the year I was in kindergarten, and of sitting in the bleachers of a giant baseball stadium in Los Angeles, with several thousand total strangers, celebrating Easter.

What I took most comfort from as a child were immediate, sensual, elemental experiences. I remember being thrilled and amazed by the world: the greenness of the grass and the sight of monarch butterflies flapping their wings in the sunlight; the smell of eucalyptus acorns and homemade cinnamon rolls still hot from the oven; the taste of corn on the cob dripping with butter and smothered in salt; the sound of the cat purring after giving birth to a litter of baby kittens in the bedroom closet; the feel of the wind on my face and the ground under my feet when I ran. I also knew the ecstacy of thinking deep thoughts and feeling honest feelings. As a child, I lived inside this elemental world, whereas the God of my understanding seemed to live outside of it: way up in the sky beyond the clouds. I wondered why that was; was there something wrong with the world that made God not want to be part of it?

The next time I remember thinking about God, I was looking out the window of a black limousine on the way to my father's funeral. It was a beautiful, Southern California day in early December, 1967. Perfect tulips lined the roadway; the grass was green, the sky cloudless; palm trees stood majestic and motionless in the distance. I was outraged that the world had not gone dark as I had—was apparently not grieving such a terrible loss. How could God allow the sun to shine and everything to continue as if it were just another day like any other? At the funeral, the minister intoned, "The Lord is my shepherd; I shall not want," and all I could think was that I *wanted* plenty. For starters, I *wanted* my father to *not* be dead. My whole frame of reference was shattered. I remember watching my mother as she swept the kitchen shortly after that, and identifying with the little particles of dirt forming a pile in the middle of the floor. My center did not seem to be holding. I felt fragmented/orphaned—abandoned by my father and God and now cursed with an acute awareness of the reality of death, in the face of which it seemed there could never be adequate comfort or consolation. I developed three vaguely articulated theories about my father's death: 1) God had killed him (It was "God's will," as a "neighbor lady" had explained to me at my father's wake); 2) I had killed him by wishing him dead; 3) He had willed himself to die. In any case, God was the one who had created the universe in which people inevitably died so I held Him ultimately responsible and determined to have nothing further to do with Him. At thirteen I became a sad and defiant atheist.

Ten years later, in the process of intensely focused and deep grieving for my father, I began to create a healing space within and around myself. The walls I had constructed in order to hold myself together after my father's death, and to cope with the process of becoming a woman in a male-dominated world, became more and more permeable until one day they suddenly dissolved/burst altogether and I found myself inside the world again, as I had been as a young child, pulsating with the ebb and flow of the elements. Waves of euphoria washed over me as rivers of tears fell from my eyes. I remained in that acutely aware, infinitely spacious state for several timeless hours until, gradually, my mind began to contract inward upon itself, shrinking back into my little ego shell. Since that time, I have never forgotten myself completely, however. Even at my most confused and self-alienated, there is always a part of me now that knows what I know and will continue to know it at all costs. In other words, I have been able to reconnect with a part of myself that is able to bear the burden of my otherness/difference, along with its attendant subjugated knowledge, without splintering under the weight of it. In fact, as my mind becomes more and more expansive, what once seemed so solid and heavy is increasingly made up of space, weighing nothing at all.

Approximately one year after my spontaneous awakening/remembering, I enrolled in a class on Buddhist philosophy at the University of Oregon. Despite my firm conviction that I "was not a religious person," enrolling in that class—taught by professor Hee-Jin Kim, who was to become a mentor for me—was something I felt inexplicably compelled to do. It was there that I first heard the Buddhist teachings of "dependent origination" and "emptiness." My sense of resonance with these teachings was so profound that upon encountering them, my mind immediately exploded in multiply orgasmic waves of delight. As I hunkered down and gripped the sides of my chair to keep from sliding into a blissful heap at professor Kim's feet, I knew I was hearing the words which corresponded to my recent experience of bursting forth/dissolving back into the elemental world. This was my own "nontheistic" version of God, I eventually decided.

Burned at the Stake

The image of being burned at the stake represents my awakening as a feminist. I returned from a year of study in Japan (1982-83)—having gone there as an undergraduate in order to immerse myself in a Buddhist culture—a committed, though unschooled, feminist. In retrospect, I realize that the rigidity of Japanese sex roles in the early 1980s—which were, in many respects, approximately thirty years behind sex role development in the U.S.—had brought me face to face with childhood memories of my parents' 1950s style relationship, and, this, in combination with the constant sexual harassment I endured there, had finally pushed me beyond denial and into an illuminating rage.

To keep the rage I felt from consuming me, I volunteered my services as a crisis phone worker at a local shelter for battered women. However, it wasn't until a year later, when I entered an interdisciplinary master's program in Women's Studies and Religious Studies, that I read my first feminist classic, Mary Daly's *Gyn/Ecology*.[2] The power of Daly's courage and brilliance was almost unbearable to me at the time. The following passage from her chapter on European witchburnings describing the maiming of mother-daughter relationships under patriarchy was especially poignant and haunting:

> ...the presence of young girls both as helpless Observers at the burnings and as legal witnesses at the trials may effectively have perpetuated the lessons of the witch craze down to this, our "own" time. Without knowing and consent women are trained to continue the ritual murder of female divinity, burning the witch within themselves and each other. (Daly, 197)

[2] Mary Daly, *Gyn/Ecology The Metaethics of Radical Feminism,* (Boston: Beacon Press, 1978)

In order to stop this silent continuation of the witchcraze, Daly argued, "it is necessary to break the silences and deceptions of 'history'" (Daly, 197). This was precisely what I had in mind on that day in 1984 as I stood before the class on World Religions about to deliver my feminist critique of same. Little did I know I would have to endure my own private witchburning in the process.

As a result of that eye-opening experience, after which, by the way, I did find my voice and manage to speak the unspeakable, I realized it was imperative that I find a way to resolve my own internalized contradictions, in particular, the one regarding self-assertion and self-sacrifice, or, ultimately, like both my parents, I would act those contradictions out in counterproductive and tragic ways. Consequently, I began looking in earnest for healthy models of relationality.

Twelve-Step literature and meetings, designed for recovery from codependency, which I began attending in 1987, were helpful to some extent. However, I soon found the apolitical and patriarchal nature of the 12-Step format limiting, and, inspired by psychologist Charlotte Kasl's feminist critique of 12-Step programs, organized my own "Feminist 13-Aspect" group for women in recovery from various things, but, ultimately, from male-domination. The group, which was made up primarily of graduate students preparing for the ministry or pursuing academic degrees in Religious Studies at the Graduate Theological Union in Berkeley, California, met for approximately a year and a half, breaking up when I moved to Santa Cruz in 1990. The first of the 13 Aspects, numbered 0 to symbolize its "ground zero" nature, stated: "We are women and we have a right to exist and to celebrate our existence through our connections with one another." Subsequent aspects interwove the personal and political dimensions of recovery and asserted the importance of surrendering fully into our "True Female Selves"—understood as the only adequate basis for liberating ourselves from male-domination. In keeping with this insight, the 11th Step of the traditional 12-Step model, advocating prayer and meditation as a means of improving "our conscious contact with God as we [understand] Him," was altered in the new Feminist 13-Aspect model to make room for such subversive and liberating practices as feminist consciousness-raising, Buddhist mindfulness meditation, and deity yoga.

Serendipitously, at around the time that the 13-Aspect group was taking shape, I became acquainted, through dreams and visions, with a female deity whom I would subsequently come to know as Green Tara of the Vajrayana Buddhist pantheon. Deity yoga practice, involving visualization of and identification with this fully enlightened goddess, has proven a powerful antidote to the insidious poison of patriarchy. Sometimes wrathful, sometimes peaceful, depending upon what is needed, she is simultaneously "self-assertive" and "self-sacrificial," passionately stepping out into the world to cut through any and all obstacles in the way of liberation for all beings, even while emptying herself of limiting ego constructs, in particular, those involving gender stereotypes. (Incidentally, I have found that when this practice is done in conjunction with mindfulness meditation, the tendency to objectify the diety as a transcendent "other" is overcome. In this way, the liberating effects of diety yoga practice are heightened.)

Though I still carry inside me the anachronistic model of a distant "God/father" who threatens to punish me whenever I dare to assert my true, untamed and unforgetting self, this oppressive image continues to wither in the face of my ongoing relationship with Tara. Perhaps the ultimate feminist, she is said to have taken a sacred vow to be reborn only in fully enlightened female form in order to counter the deluded notion of female inferiority at the deepest possible level.

Two years have passed since I finished my dissertation and received my Ph.D. in Comparative Religion and Women's Studies from the Graduate Theological Union in Berkeley. Qualitatively, much has happened in these two short years. Immediately after graduating, I taught for a year in Michigan, then relocated to Eugene, Oregon, where I am a self-employed writer/educator/editor/counselor. Last summer, a particularly heartfelt relationship ended abruptly, propelling me into the kind of grief that went beyond my immediate circumstances into a timeless, bottomless, boundaryless place. From that vantage point, I was forced to admit that despite my best efforts—including years of spiritual practice, feminist consciousness-raising, and therapy—each time the possibility of a"soul mated" love had emerged for me I was not ready. In fact, I had failed to attract a partner worthy of the name "mature adult." I had a newly-minted Ph.D., the promise of a rich and rewarding career, a circle of magnificent friends, a good brain, a good heart, and, at forty-one, reasonably good health, but the kind of personal fulfillment that comes from truly committed, long-term partnership with a kindred spirit had constantly eluded me.

And so I finally gave up. From deep within myself the following prayer, addressed to no one in particular, arose: "Please help me surrender into my destiny, whatever that may be. And, if, for the sake of all beings, it's best that I be alone, please help me find the strength and courage to accept my aloneness." With those words, a sense of entitlement I hadn't even known was there suddenly evaporated and with it feelings of bitterness, frustration, and despair that had crowded out my peace of mind, obscured my vision, and impaired my judgment. And, for the first time in a long time, I was completely at peace with my life. It seemed as if I were at the bottom of a deep, cool well on a sweltering summer day, with nowhere left to fall, nothing left to lose. From that place, every breath was a sacred gift, every act somehow already complete.

So, of course, since I was no longer trying to force the issue in any way, a few days later I met the man who had been holding the other half of my heart in safe keeping. Together we began a life which I can only describe as "mutual surrender into our shared destiny," our "one shared heart." John is a healer of Native American ancestry on his mother's side whose shamanic abilities have developed over the course of the last twenty-five years of disciplined spiritual practice and apprenticeship. In the process of emptying himself of preconceived notions and attachments to things being any particular way, he has become increasingly able to see things more as they truly are.

In the synergy of our connection, I have begun to reclaim my own latent psychic abilities. In the process of seeing clients with John and looking as deeply as possible into the roots of their suffering, many of my long-held assumptions and insights have been tested and clarified. For example, it appears more true to me now than ever that the whole point of existence, whether human or otherwise, is to realize and express our true natures which are inherently luminous, radiant, spacious, relational, interdependent, wise, compassionate, whole, and complete.

Furthermore, it seems that of all the options available to us, birth in the human realm is most conducive to such realization, for several reasons. First of all, without the type of self-consciousness that comes with human birth, though we would certainly continue to *be* our Selves, we would not have the potential to *know* our Selves. Paradoxically, human self-consciousness entails both the tendency to experience ourselves as separate or inherently different from other beings, and, ultimately, the desire and ability to overcome this tendency. As we are born into this conditioned world of, at best, approximately equal parts pain and pleasure, we instinctively strive to avoid painful experiences while clinging to pleasurable ones. In this way, we create much suffering for ourselves.

Talk about your classic existential crisis! Over countless lifetimes we evolve to the point of readiness for the rare opportunity of human birth, the "most precious of all births," but by the time we have arrived here, which includes for most of us a somewhat disorienting trip down the birth canal, we have either forgotten why we chose this place to begin with or try to renig on the experience altogether, out of a misguided sense of inadequacy and unworthiness. Once here, we devise various more or less ingenious strategies for distracting ourselves from the deep undertow of our existence, the primal pull toward surrender into our destinies, the final realization of what it means to be both fully human and fully divine.

Sadly, most of us die out of this world without ever having been fully born into it. We are only partially here, holding our breaths against the uncertainties and limitations which are an inevitable part of the human condition, looking toward the future for those all too fleeting moments of comfort and security—imperfect because, though real, they do not last—or skyward toward some transcendent and final resting place, capable of absolving us of responsibility for our own evolution—indeed, for the evolution of consciousness, itself.

Adding insult to injury, gravity can seem like such a drag. After months of floating around in the relative weightlessness of the womb, and who knows how long before that drifting along in some transmigratory subtle body, described in esoteric forms of Buddhism as seven times lighter than our physical bodies, we find ourselves lying flat on our backs with no neck muscles to speak of and heads the size and weight of small bowling balls. And that's only the beginning of a lifetime of lessons learned through unrelenting exposure to this immutable law.

Surrender seems the great, universal cure all for just about everything that ails us, but let me make clear what I mean by this. I do not mean that we should surrender to oppressive conditions, poverty, cruelty, sexism, unnatural disease processes, dangerous living conditions, or injustice of any kind. I also do not advocate surrendering to someone else's notion of what is best for us or to "God's" will, if God is understood as someone other than our true selves. Authentic surrender does not tolerate abuse, nor does it foster frustration, bitterness, burnout, or violence, because it derives from that place within us where we can never be diminished, degraded, or desecrated in any way and because it is unattached to the fruits of its labor. It is not wimpy, passive, overly-sentimental, codependent, or spaced-out. It is also not the polar opposite of self-assertion, understood in ruggedly individualistic terms.

Instead, surrender involves a gradual opening to the luminous, radiant, spacious, exquisite depths of our beings, into the beings we are destined to become and, paradoxically have always been, allowing us to be at ease in impermanence, to be fully at peace within the confines of the human condition. To the extent our precious human and spiritual resources are no longer being syphoned off by the impulse to flee, we are unleashed for passionate activity and engagement with the world. Such activity is undertaken for the sake of all beings, including one's self, for it is understood that there is really no such thing as individual liberation. Until all are free of suffering, none are free of suffering.

Our parents seem to play an important role in helping us surrender into our destinies. It appears that we choose our parents for certain "lineage transmissions" they have agreed to provide for us. Such transmissions are usually unskillfully delivered and unskillfully received, causing much frustration and brokenheartedness. Once we are able to distinguish the original transmission from the unskillful way in which it is delivered, however, we can surrender into and fully receive the intended gift with an open heart. For example, my father's gift to me was an ache for spiritual perfection, in itself a beautiful thing, which, unfortunately, took the form of a kind of narrow perfectionism, causing me to feel that I was never good enough. My mother, on the other hand, unskillfully imparted to me the gift of unwavering discernment regarding bullshit of any kind. While I have come to deeply appreciate these gifts, I have had to learn to separate the enlightened core of each from the unenlightened energy associated with them.

An especially poignant and powerful practice I have developed in the last few months involves prostrating myself before pictures of my parents placed on my altar, in gratitude for what they so ineptly tried to give and what I so ineptly tried to receive. More healing has been accomplished through this simple practice than through anything else I can think of. I am often spontaneously moved to recommend this practice to my clients, with dramatic results.

I recall the words of a Zen Buddhist therapist I once knew, who, upon hearing story after story, week after week, of my unfortunate involvements with various, seemingly interchangeable men—each of whom professed to love strong women in theory though unable to do so in practice—compassionately shook his head, saying: "More suffering is evidently necessary." I am happy to finally report that "No more suffering is evidently necessary," at least not of the sort that has, in the past, undermined my self-esteem and robbed me of precious energy better used in the quest for spiritual awakening and socio-political liberation.

I always knew this kind of life was possible. The biggest challenge I have these days is to surrender each day into the goodness and bigness of it, to know myself worthy of my own destiny, of my own unique expression of liberation within this very world, gravity and all.

Yvonne Vowels

TWO OF HEARTS

We two,
One shared heart...
This is how
It shall be:
A single lotus
bursting forth
Into the very Mind
Of God;
Beloved twin souls
Reinhabiting the Womb
Of all wombs.

This unbearable ache,
Birth pangs
Of an ancient remembrance
Calling us home.
This breath,
Our shimmering entry
Into a place
Before space and time
Where we have never
Been apart.
This astonishing love,
Too immense
To be born in solitude.
This burning,
Surely an eternal flame.

Kissing Kisses Kissing
In exquisite meditation,
And we know we are blessed
Beyond knowing;
Know we have touched
Beyond touching.

You, my mountain lion,
Newly born,
I, your Goddess,
Unveiled.
Already married
In service and devotion.
Surrendering
Even surrender, itself
In the realization
Of our destiny.

All beings weep with joy
While angels sing
For the amazing grace
Of our reunion.
The universe conspires
To awaken to itself
In and through our love making.
And we,
Who have taken birth
For just this moment,
At last come to rest
Deep in our
One shared heart...

Claudia E. Lapp

DARNING THE WORLD

Opening my mother's sewing box,
of inlaid wood, from Germany,
makes me infinitely sad.
It happens each time:
the small familiar tools,
the same ones she handled,
speak of her in thimble and thread language
in accents of wartime wartime wartime
lost buttons, torn hems, severed arms.

And tonight is the night.
The sock will be darned.
The proper needle, the correct thread color
falls into my nimble hands.
It goes well for once, the darning.
The hole yields to surgery, closes stitch by stitch,
smoothly, without a lump to cause discomfort.
Does my mother's spirit preside?
It makes me infinitely sad,
for in that sewing box nestle all women,
darning, tending the small mendings for daughters,
for sons, for mates they're missing, for those
who've been missed and will be missed and missing forever
the world over and over again and darning still, in peace
and war and peace repairing the world, pulling it together,
thread by thread, re-piecing it, with love and devotion.

The world needs a good darning.
The heart of the world needs the sewing box of women
to close the wound, pull one side to the other,
in peace, one piece, repaired, IN PAX.

Amy Klauke-Minato

THE WIDER LENS

Although the way we study detaches
bud from twig, fossil from lake, still
I have not learned to separate
the dropped pine cone from its quilt
of fir and maple leaf, trout fin
from river rock, birdsong from
dawn light. Nor could I sever
rainsmell from barefeet, snowfall
from red cheek, or the lake
from the wind combing its skin.
I can not seem to untangle
the arms of the manzanita,
from the horizon's gray waist. Because
the speckled gall changes once it slips
from its shelf of oak bark to rot
on mud ridge and twig scatter. And
the curled fawn isn't the same without
the calyx of grass against which it rests,
or the hemlock beyond that, any less the owl
in its top branch asleep with yellow eye open
on the mouse to be churned into a furred
pellet and spit out beneath
the dark cape and its
circling aperture
taking it all in.

ELDERS

—for Dot Fisher-Smith

Nobody told her
to lock herself
with a bike chain
to the logging truck
but when the forest service
workers stopped arguing
with "them darn tree-huggers"
there she was
five feet tall, tanned and tough
as a nut, smiling serenely,
locked to their immense
vehicle. It was quiet

as a church but for the rain
dripping off the needles
of the 500 year old trees
and plopping in the mud
created by the road
created for the machines
come to cut them down
and for the trucks
to cart them off.

A steller's jay cocked
its imperial crest
at the crowd and a pacific giant
salamander contemplated justice
from beneath a sword fern.
The scene was recorded
in the vast eyes of the tiny spotted owl
deep in the forest and captured
in the spread cape of the catapulting
flying squirrel high
in the canopy and inscribed
in the locked arms and open hearts
of the small tribe
of chilled but firm protesters. "Hell,"
one of the officials said, "it's late."

Besides, this white-haired lady
looked like any of their grandmas
or Mother Teresa so the driver
kicked a rotting log inhabited
by nematodes, bark beetles,
sphagnum moss, bracken fern,
and the tottering seedlings
of mountain hemlock offering
to leave if she would please
unlock herself from his truck

"But first tell me," he pleaded
"you look like a nice lady, *why*
did you do that?" She looked up
at him, rain following
the paths of wrinkles
down her face, "Because"
she said, nodding toward the trees,
"they were here first."

WEEKLY SERVICE

Peer beneath the rotten
sheath of cedar bark for the subways
of mites, ants, centipedes and there make
the sign of the circle. Find
where the gills of the oyster
mushroom radiate beneath
its thick umbrella, and bless that place.
Bow at the base of the nitrogen-fixing
alder and lupine and pour sacred water on
the back of the slate gray grub feeding
on the new leaves of the ash. Make
a pilgrimage to the freckled feathers on the belly
of the red-shafted flicker and chant
about tree cover, about sky. Uncover
the weasel's den where the bones of
its supper splay in triangles
on the dirt. Do homage. Dip your first two
fingers into the frog pond and smudge algae
on your brow. Now, take your place
in the cathedral. And listen for the omniscient
note of the elusive Coyote, scrawny
on the cliff. Then kneel
on the mulch and offer
alms of flesh to the fat bishop,
the possum waddling on pink feet,
coming to collect.

CONTRIBUTORS' NOTES

Kim Addonizio is the author of two poetry collections: *The Philosopher's Club* (1993) and *Jimmy & Rita* (1997), both from BOA Editions. A chapbook of her poetry appears in *Sextet One* from Pennywhistle Press (1996). Her fiction can be found in *Breaking Up Is Hard To Do, Chelsea, Chick-Lit, Gettysburg Review, Microfictions,* and elsewhere. She is currently working on a collection of stories and a novel. She lives in San Francisco.

Thomas Avena received a 1995 American Book Award for editing and co-writing *Life Sentences: Writers, Artists, and AIDS* (Mercury House, 1994). Mr. Avena was the writer-in-residence and editor for "Project Face to Face," the AIDS oral-history and arts project, during its installation in the Smithsonian Institute's Experimental Gallery. In 1994, he was awarded both the International Humanitas Award for his work in AIDS education and the arts, and the Joseph Henry Jackson Award for literature for *Dream of Order* (Mercury House, 1997). He is co-editor with Adam Klein of *Jerome, After the Pageant* (Bastard Books/D.A.P., 1996), a monograph on the controversial and visionary paintings of Jerome Caja. Mr. Avena lives in San Francisco.

Ellyn Bache has authored five books. Her first two novels, *Safe Passage* and *Festival in Fire Season,* were both Literary Guild and Doubleday Book Club selections, and *Safe Passage* was made into a feature film starring Susan Sarandon. Her nonfiction book, *Culture Clash,* is about her experiences helping a Vietnamese refugee family resettle in America; and her short story collection, *The Value of Kindness* (Helicon Nine Editions, 1993), won the Willa Cather Fiction Prize. Bache's newest novel, *The Activist's Daughter,* is forthcoming from Spinsters Ink in spring 1997. She lives with her family in Wilmington, North Carolina.

Marilyn J. Boe writes poetry in Bloomington, Minnesota. Her work has appeared in numerous literary reviews and anthologies, including *Poetry East, Poets On: Healing,* and *Earth's Daughters.* She has also published six chapbooks of poetry.

Laure-Anne Bosselaar moved to the United States from Belgium in 1986. She holds an M. F. A. from the Warren Wilson Program for Writers. Among other publications, her work has appeared in *The Massachusetts Review, Denver Quarterly, International Quarterly, Salamander, Sycamore Review, Nimrod,* and *The Spoon River Poetry Review.* Her book, *The Hour Between Dog and Wolf,* will be published by BOA Editions in Spring of 1997.

Donna J. Braswell-Mussato is "an old poet," born in Oak Park, Illinois in 1941. She has kept diaries and journals all her life. Now, from her writing room, she looks through oak trees, writes and remembers. She has two poems forthcoming in *Hard Boot,* an anthology about Kentucky, edited by Vivian Shipley (Negative Capability Press).

Jayne Relaford Brown performs her work, makes paper, gardens and teaches writing, literature and women's studies in the San Diego area. Her poetry has appeared in such periodicals as *The Minnesota Review, Pacific Review, Hurricane Alice, Common Lives/Lesbian Lives,* and in several anthologies, including *I Am Becoming the Woman I've Wanted; Wanting Women: Erotic Les-*

bian Poetry; The Poetry of Sex: Lesbians Write the Erotic; Silver-Tongued Sapphistry and *El Vuelo del Aguila/The Flight of the Eagle.* Her fiction has been published in *Dykescapes* by Alyson Press. Brown lives with her lover of five years in the suburbs of San Diego County and is the mother of three adult children.

Camincha is from Miraflores, Lima, Peru where she returns often to remain close to her roots, although she calls the U. S. her second home. Her poetry and fiction have appeared in both English and Spanish in*Morena, Northwest Literary Forum, Visions International* and in the *Pacifica Tribune,* among others. As well, she has produced two bilingual books, a collection of poems, *Where I Come from, Where I am Going / Donde Vengo, A Donde Voy* (1992), and a collection of short fiction, *Indecent Exposure/ Exhibición Impúdica* (1993). Of her work, the *San Francisco Bay Guardian* has written, "Camincha frames the ordinary in a way that makes it extraordinary, and that is real talent."

John R. Campbell's poems and essays have appeared or are forthcoming in *Poetry, North American Review, Sewanee Review, Poetry East, Seattle Review, Northwest Review,* and many other literary journals. He is the author of two volumes of poetry, *Intimate Distance* and *Lives of the Saints,* as well as two collections of essays, *Absence and Light: Meditations from the Klamath Marshes* and *Domestic Waters: Searching for Home in the American West.* He is currently at work on a book-length poem entitled *The Far West.*

Janine Canan is a poet and psychiatrist, founder of Port Townsend's Center for Integration, member of the Worldwide Women's Party, and devotee of the Divine Mother. Her seven books include *Her Magnificent Body: New & Selected Poems* and *She Rises like the Sun: Invocations of the Goddess by Contemporary American Women Poets,* recipient of the 1990 Koppelman Award. Canan's writings have appeared in dozens of anthologies, including *American Poets Say Goodbye to the Twentieth Century* and *The Divine Feminine.* A new collection of her poems, *Changing Woman,* and a series of short stories, *Journeys with Justine,* will soon be published.

Melissa Capers writes, "I'm a recent émigré from Virginia into Austin, TX. The wide open bright blue sky in Austin is still dazzling, as is the mix of clarity and compassion from the folks I've met so far. I'm working on a novel, which should be finished this year, and looking for part-time work and ways to teach. "

Marilyn Elain Carmen's essay is dedicated to her great grandmother, Mariah Johnson, and to two Cherokee women, Florence Felton and Geneva Felton Scruggs, her mother and grandmother, who lived with family violence. It is with the aid and guidance of their spirits that she has been able to thrive. Her writing has been published widely in the United States, Canada and England, and her novella, *Blood at the Root,* was published by Esoterica in 1990, the year she also received a grant from the Pennsylvania State Council on the Arts. Currently, she teaches at the Community College of Philadelphia.

Nancy Casey lives in the country near Moscow, Idaho, with her partner, two children, a dog, three cats, a pair of sheep and a half-dozen chickens. She writes, "Nobody could ever say that my life is boring. This year, I spent a month in Haiti. Later on, my best friend went insane and my house burned—all in the same week. I write nonfiction because life is so amazing. I write about what I do, what happens to me, and what I think. What to make of it? This is living. That is all I can say."

Renny Christopher has been married to Vietnam veterans twice, and has been a member of a vets' partners' rap group. She is the author of a poetry collection, *Viet Nam and California* (Burning Cities Press). She teaches English at Cabrillo Community College.

Elizabeth Claman's poetry chapbook, *Peripheral Visions*, was published by Five Fingers Press in 1989. The same year, she won the Grand Prize in *Negative Capability*'s Eve of Saint Agnes poetry competition, judged by Diane Wakoski. She has also won other awards, including two grants from Oregon's Literary Arts Foundation, an Oregon Humanities Fellowship, a Jane Grant Dissertation Award, and a scholarship to Squaw Valley Community of Writers. Her poetry and fiction have appeared in many literary reviews, most recently in *River Styx, Hurricane Alice* and *Two Girls Review*. Currently, in addition to editing anthologies for Queen of Swords Press and fiction for the *Northwest Review*, she is completing a Ph. D. in Comparative Literature at the University of Oregon.

Lanora L. Cox is struggling to transform her dream of being a writer into a reality. Early on she believed writers had to experience what they wrote about, so she set off to experience other cultures and altered states. These days she waits tables and volunteers on a Crisis and Suicide Hotline in Oakland, California, while writing about all she has learned from her adventures.

Alice Crane is the pen-name of a Northwest writer whose work appeared previously in *James River Review* (West Virginia) and *Writing Our Way out of the Dark* (Queen of Swords Press, 1995).

Barbara Crooker has published poems in many periodicals, such as *The Denver Quarterly, Yankee, The Christian Science Monitor, Poets On, The Pennsylvania Review* and *The Madison Review.* Her work has also appeared in a number of anthologies, including *If I Had a Hammer: Women's Work in Poetry and Fiction* and *The Tie That Binds: Mothers and Sons/Fathers and Daughters,* both from Papier Mache, and *Life on the Line* from Negative Capability Press. She has been the recipient of awards and grants from the NEA and the Pennsylvania Council On The Arts. The poems included in *Hard Love* were written about a close friend whom she supported in her efforts to leave an abusive marriage. Crooker writes, "I'm not a stranger to suffering, but I also believe in the healing power of love and redemption."

Martha Clark Cummings' collection of short stories, *Mono Lake,* was published by Row Barge Press in 1995 and her novel, *Current Issues and Enduring Questions,* is forthcoming. She lives in Thermopolis, Wyoming, with her partner, the writer, Lisa Vice. Cummings has been the recipient of an Astreaea Foundation Lesbian Writers Fund Emerging Writer's Award for 1994, the Barbara Demming Memorial Fund Grant in Fiction (1990), and a New York Foundation for the Arts Fellowship Award in Fiction (1990). Her writings have appeared in *Common Lives/Lesbian Lives Quarterly, Sojourner, Hurricane Alice, North Atlantic Review,* and the anthology, *Love's Shadow* (Crossing Press, 1993).

Philip Dacey is the author of five books of poetry, the most recent being *Night Shift at the Crucifix Factory* (U. of Iowa, 1991). He co-edited, with David Jauss, *Strong Measures: Contemporary American Poetry in Traditional Forms* (HarperCollins, 1986). Divorced, 55, and a part-time teacher, he has three children, who live in St. Paul, Minnesota; Olympia, Washington; and Dublin, Ireland. He says the sixth decade of his life is the best yet.

Dee DeGeiso has been an English teacher, a school psychologist, a non–practicing attorney, and a legal writing instructor. Now, finally, she is devoting herself full–time to creative writing. A member of Amherst Writers and Artists, she has recently begun leading writing workshops, and is simultaneously working on a novel, a collection of stories, and a series of poems dealing with women's concerns at various life stages. She and her husband are attempting to collaborate on a mystery. Currently she is also the Co-Director of the Northampton Film Festival in Northampton, Massachusetts.

Social activist, feminist and poet, **Sue Doro** was also a railway machinist for thirteen years. Her poems and prose have been published in the *Village Voice, Chicago Tribune, Washington Post,* and various women's and labor magazines as well as anthologies such as *If I Had A Hammer* (1992) and *I Am Becoming The Woman I've Wanted* (1994), both from Papier Mache Press, and *Liberating Memory* (Rutgers University Press, 1995). Her work has also been published in several scholastic publications in the U. S., Canada, and Norway including textbooks such as *Literature Across Cultures* (Simon & Schuster, Inc. 1994), and *English At Work* (Gyldendal Norsk Forlag A/S 1994) and *The Language of Literature* (McDougal Littell, 1996). Doro is also the author of three books on her blue collar work experience and its relationship to family and personal life: *Of Birds And Factories* (1982), *Heart Home and Hard Hats* (Midwest Villages and Voices 1986), and *Blue Collar Goodbyes* (Papier Mache Press 1993).

Sharon Doubiago was born in Long Beach, California. She holds an M. A. in English from California State University at Los Angeles. For many years she has traveled the American West as an itinerant writer and teacher, staking out a unique territory for herself as a feminist, scholar and poet. Her books of poetry and fiction include *Hard Country* (West End, 1982), *The Book of Seeing with One's Own Eyes* (Graywolf, 1988) and *South America Mi Hija* (University of Pittsburgh Press, 1992), among many others. Doubiago has won numerous grants and awards and is a highly sought-after reader and performer of her poems all over the United States.

Alice Evans is a freelance journalist, poet and fiction writer. Her work has appeared in *Poets & Writers* magazine, as well as in two Seal Press anthologies, *Another Wilderness* (edited by Susan Fox Rogers, 1994) and *Solo* (Rogers, 1996).

Molly Fisk lives in Nevada City, California. She is the poetry editor for the quarterly, *Estero,* and teaches poetry at Marin County's Juvenile Hall and with California Poets in the Schools. Her manuscript, *Listening to Winter,* has been a Walt Whitman Award and National Poetry Series finalist, and her profile of writer Anne Lamott has just appeared in *Poets & Writers* magazine.

Sarah Fox is 30, and lives in Milwaukee with her 6 year old daughter, Nora. Since becoming divorced over five years ago, she has returned to school where she earned her B. A. Degree in English in 1994. She hopes to do graduate work in Creative Writing. Her poems have appeared in *The Wisconsin Academy Review, Exquisite Corpse, Sojourner, Poetry Motel* and several local anthologies.

Laura Goodman's recent work has appeared in *Other Voices, The Worcester Review,* and *South Dakota Review.* Previously, her writings have appeared in *Crosscurrents, Pikestaff Forum, Sing Heavenly Muse,* and elsewhere. With her husband and son she lives and writes in the foothills of Boulder, Colorado.

Barbara Hendryson grew up and still lives in the San Francisco Bay area. She studied writing in San Francisco State University's graduate Creative Writing Program with the late William Dickey. Her poems have appeared in many literary reviews, most recently *The Alaska Quarterly, The Bellingham Review, The Berkeley Poetry Review, Kalliope,* and the *Southern Poetry Review.* She has also been published in a number of important anthologies on the issue of healing, including *Writing Our Way Out of the Dark* from Queen of Swords Press (1995), *Sixteen Voices* (Mariposa Press, 1994) and *Cries of the Spirit* (Beacon Press, 1992). In addition, her work has also won several well-deserved awards, from the Chester H. Jones Foundation, Peninsula Community Foundation, among others.

Robin Jacobson is a consultant to writers and publishers. Formerly a voice/acting coach and director, she trained at Eastman School of Music and the Center for the Study of Relationship (Boston Gestalt Institute), and is a certified practitioner of the Rubenfeld Synergy Method. Weaving these threads, Robin teaches "Coming to Your Senses: A Body-Mind Workshop for Poets & Writers." Her poetry has appeared in *Barnabe Mountain Review, Poets On,* and *Talking Raven,* and is forthcoming in *Tricycle: The Buddhist Review* (online). She was recently awarded an affiliateship and writing studio at the Headlands Center for the Arts in Sausalito, California.

Leigh Anne Jasheway is a humor writer, stand-up comic, and stress management consultant, in Eugene, Oregon. Her humorous takes on life have been published in the *Los Angeles Times, Comic News, Women's Harpoon, Hysteria,* and many others. She draws extensively from her dysfunctional family life in creating healing humor. She writes, for example, "My Mom has been married five times. Not to be outdone, my Dad has also been married five times. Our family photo takes up the whole mantle, and every other person's face is blacked out. . . . Holidays were cheap around our house. We didn't want to spend much on each other because we were pretty sure that come next year we weren't even going to be related."

Andrea King Kelly is a Kingsbury Writing Fellow in the Ph.D. program in English at Florida State University, where she received the 1991 John Mackay Shaw Academy of American Poets Award. Over the past few years she has been the recipient of the 1992 Hemingway Short Story Prize, and the 1993 Phi Kappa Phi Artist Award. She has also served on the Board of Directors for Anhinga Press, and as poetry editor for *IQ: International Quarterly.* Her writing has appeared most recently in *Puerto del Sol , Amelia* and *Rosebud.*

Katie Kingston has published poetry in several literary magazines including *Puerto del Sol, Blue Mesa Review, Ellipsis, the eleventh MUSE,* and *Weber Studies.* Her poetry has also appeared in several anthologies, and she has presented readings of her work in Vermont, Colorado, and Utah. She is a graduate of the Vermont College M. F. A. program in creative writing, and currently teaches poetry at Trinidad State Junior College in Colorado. She is also the grant director for the *Corazon de Trinidad Reading Series* and poetry editor for the *Purgatoire,* a campus literary magazine.

Although primarily a poet, **Amy Klauke-Minato** also writes children's stories and creative nonfiction. She holds an MS in Environmental Studies from the University of Oregon. Currently, she teaches Environmental Studies at the UO, works as a naturalist educator for Nearby Nature in Eugene, Oregon, and is an educational consultant for the University of Oregon Museum of Natural History. She has also worked as an associate poetry editor for the *Northwest Review*. Her writing has appeared in *Cottonwood Magazine, Cimarron Review, Wild Earth*, and *Seneca Review*, among others.

Claudia E. Lapp, a refugee from the East Coast, has been living in Eugene, Oregon since 1991. A graduate of Bennington College, she published her first poetry in Montreal, where she taught at John Abbott College. Her poems have appeared in many anthologies: *Montreal English Poets Of The Seventies, The Véhicule Poets, Sounds Like, Cross/Cut, Free State, Animus Aeternus, Véhicule Days*. her book, *Cloud Gate,* was published in 1985. Most recently, she has received a Morgan Arts Council grant for a week-long poetry residency in Berkeley Springs, West Virginia in November 1996.

Dorianne Laux is the author of two collections of poetry from BOA Editions, *Awake* (1990) and *What We Carry* (1994) which was a finalist for the National Book Critics Circle Award. She is also the recipient of a Pushcart Prize for poetry and a fellowship from The National Endowment for the Arts. In 1994 she joined the faculty at the University of Oregon's Program in Creative Writing. Recent poems have been published in *The Harvard Review, The Alaska Quarterly Review* and *The American Poetry Review*. Her poetry can also be heard on National Public Radio's "The Writer's Almanac," hosted by Garrison Keillor. Presently she is at work on a new book of poems, tentatively entitled *Music in the Morning*.

Rachel Loden's poems have appeared in *New American Writing, College English, New York Quarterly*, and *The Prose Poem*, among other magazines, and are forthcoming in *Seneca Review, Graham House Review, Onthebus, Caliban*, and others. She lives in Palo Alto, California, with her husband and daughter, and works with private poetry students.

Katharyn Howd Machan teaches in the Writing a Program at Ithaca College, belly dances with Mirage Dance Troupe, and serves on the Board of Directors of the Feminist Women's Writing Workshops. With her husband and fellow poet, Eric Machan Howd, her hours are also devoted to parenting CoraRose and Benjamin. She has published 18 collections of poems, most recently, *Belly Words* (Sometimes Y Publications, 1994) and *The Professor Poems* (Adrienne Lee Press, 1996).

Chris Mandell wrote her poem on the Ides of March, 1988. Her work has appeared in a number of reviews and anthologies, including *What's a Nice Girl Like You Doing in a Relationship Like This*. She lives in Massachusetts

Lisa Martinovic´ has been published in magazines and anthologies from coast to coast. The author of five chapbooks, her greatest passion is performing poetry: from cafes in San Francisco's Mission District to Lollapalooza in New Orleans and the Austin International Poetry Festival. Lisa was a mere guppy in the San Francisco poetry scene. Upon moving to Hogeye, Arkansas she mutated into some bizarre species of Ozark Slam Shark. No venue is safe! Recently, she has taken to performing with pythons and cheap fireworks. Nevertheless, she won a spot on the Ozark National Slam team for the second year in a row.

Joseph Millar lives in Mill Valley, California, with his eleven year old son, Daniel, and works as a telephone installer foreman. His work has appeared in *DoubleTake, Jacaranda, Manoa, Mudfish* and the *Steelhead Special*. This year his poetry won the Montalvo Biennial Poetry Competition, judged by Garrett Hongo, and placed Second in the National Writer's Union Competition, judged by Philip Levine.

Adam David Miller, whose third book of verse, *My Trip is Not Your Trip,* will be out soon from Eshu House Publishing, is also author of *Neighborhood and Other Poems* (Mina Press, 1993) and *Forever Afternoon* (Michigan State University Press, 1994), winner of the Naomi Long Madgett Poetry Award. His next venture will be in semi-autobiographical fiction. He lives in Berkeley, California.

Blake More writes, "Fortunately I am no longer stuck in a cycle of violence; I owe much of my healing to poetry. I know if I hadn't had the courage to pick up my pen and write—to see my blood in ink—I would never have found the strength to seek therapy, stop starving myself and end the relationships that perpetuated my pain." Currently, More lives in Northern California where she earns her living writing articles for such magazines as the *Yoga Journal* and *Tokyo Time Out*. Her book, *Headache Free: Alternative Medical Solutions to Headaches* will be on bookstore shelves any day now.

Judith Neva teaches Liberal Studies at the University of Montana in Missoula, where she also received her M. F. A. in poetry. Under an NEH grant, she is working on a project entitled, "Pathographies: A Study of Illness Narratives." Her poems have appeared in such journals as *Seattle Review, Visions International, Blue Mesa Review, Thema, Pegasus, Northern Lights, Intermountain Woman* and *Sow's Ear.*

"Things Are Close to the Surface Here" comes out of **Valerie Nieman**'s work as reporter, now city editor, for a small daily newspaper in West Virginia. Her poetry and fiction have appeared in magazines such as *New Virginia Review, Poetry* and *New Letters,* and anthologies including the Queen of Swords anthology, *Each in Her Own Way, Women Writing on the Menopause*. A chapbook, *Slipping Out of Old Eve,* was published by *Sing Heavenly Muse!* Works-in-progress include a novel set in 11th-century Scotland and a collection of short fiction. A graduate of West Virginia University, she is a founding co-editor of the literary magazine *Kestrel: A Journal of Art and Literature in the New World.*

With an M.A. in writing, **Elizabeth Oakley** writes poetry, fiction and children's stories. Her work has been published in several anthologies and journals, and she also teaches writing.

Martha W. Ostheimer is a graduate of the M.F.A. program at the University of Arizona where she is currently an Adjunct Lecturer in Writing and Creativity in the Electrical and Computer Engineering Department. Her poems have appeared twice in the *Madison Review,* and in *80 on the 80s: A Decade's History in Verse* (Ashland Poetry Press). She is currently working on a novel, and is joyously married.

Born and raised in Detroit (Michigan, not Oregon), **Christina Pacosz** moved to Eagle Creek, Oregon in the early '70s, and has been on the road ever since. She writes poetry and prose in Surfside Beach, South Carolina. Her books of poetry include *Shimmy Up to This Fine Mud* (Poets Warehouse, 1975), and *This Is Not a Place to Sing* (West End, 1987). She has been a poet/writer in the schools/community for the Portland Metropolitan Arts Commission, and a visiting artist in North Carolina. In addition, she has received grants from the Washington State Arts Commission, the Alaska State Council on the Arts, and the South Carolina Arts Commission.

Linda Peavy recently received an M.F.A. in fiction writing from Washington University, where she also studied play writing. Her work, *Dinah's Song*, a choreopoem , is based on a woman's struggle to overcome the damage of childhood sexual abuse. "The Kill Floor" is based on the story told her by a Montana woman whose daughter was being stalked by an abusive husband. She notes that "violence has no geographical boundaries." Over the past twenty-five years she has published nine books of non-fiction, five of them co-authored by Ursula Smith, the most recent of which is *Women in Waiting in the Westward Movement: Life on the Home Frontier*. (University of Oklahoma Press, 1994).

Andrea Potos lives in Madison, Wisconsin. Her poems have recently appeared in *Calyx*, and in two anthologies, *I Feel a Little Jumpy Around You*, edited by Naomi Shihab Nye and Paul Janezck (Simon and Schuster), and *Claiming the Spirit Within* (Beacon Hill Press, 1996).

Amudha Rajendran is a Tamil/Telugu writer of prose and poetry. She resides in Queens, New York, happily. She is the recipient of the 1994 Audre Lorde Memorial Award for a manuscript of poems. She is currently working on a novel entitled *Seven Eleven*. In the future, she will have two poems published in *The Western Humanities Review* and three poems published in *Excursus*. She believes that everything will turn out just fine.

Glynnis Reed is a twenty-year-old college student, currently living in Los Angeles, California. She is a poet and visual artist who is committed to the challenge of doing cultural work.

Holly Lu Conant Rees is a feminist, Quaker, vegetarian, and mother of a wondrous eleven year-old. She's had poems published in *Sojourner, Frontiers* and the *Birmingham Poetry Review*. Her paid work is with a parent support network for families who have a child with special needs, as she does.

Elisavietta Ritchie's *Flying Time: Stories & Half–Stories* includes four PEN Syndicated Fiction winners. Her poetry collections include *The Arc of the Storm; Elegy for the Other Woman: new & selected terribly female poems; A Wound–Up Cat and Other Bedtime Stories; Raking The Snow; Tightening The Circle Over Eel Country*. She is also the editor of *The Dolphin's Arc: Poems on Endangered Creatures of the Sea, Finding The Name*, and other books.

Emily Robertson's poetry is about Love and being Black. She writes, "While I enjoy reliving and creating beautiful erotic moments in my poetry, I also feel strongly that domestic abuse must be discussed and explored." Emily is 23 years old and attends the University of Washington in Seattle. The poems presented here are from her collection, *Afrodisiac*

Willa Schneberg's first book of poems, entitled *Box Dreams*, was published by alice james books. Widely published in literary reviews, she has also won a number of awards for her writing, including the 1992 second prize in the Allen Ginsberg Poetry Competition and a 1994 grant from Oregon's Literary Arts. In 1995 she was a finalist in the national Writers' Union Poetry Competition, judged by Philip Levine. In 1994, she went to Cambodia where she worked with the United Nations' Transitional Authority, assisting them conduct "free and fair elections." Her second book, drawn from these and other travel experiences, has been a finalist in several competitions.

Bárbara Selfridge's list of publications is finally longer than her arrest record. She's received fellowships from the NEA, the Fine Arts Work Center in Provincetown, and Poets and Writers. Her stories have appeared in anthologies and magazines including *The Carribean Writer, The American Voice, Ploughshares*, and *The Pushcart Prizes, 1993*. Her Puerto Rico based collection of stories, *Surrounded by Water*, is looking for a home.

Brenda Shaw grew up in New England, received a Doctorate in Biology from Boston University, then lived a number of years in Scotland where she worked as a scientist and lecturer at Dundee University Medical School. Her fiction, poetry and essays have been published on both sides of the Atlantic. A collection of her poems, *The Cold Winds of Summer*, was published in Scotland in 1987 by Blind Serpent Press. *The Dark Well*, a book-length memoir, is just out from Audenreed Press.

Elizabeth Sinclaire is presently pursuing a Master's Degree in Counseling at Lewis and Clark College in Portland, Oregon. She holds an M. F. A. in Creative Writing from University of Oregon and has been published in Northwest journals and magazines. She has had a varied background, working as a firefighter, college teacher, archaeologist, and writer/seeker. Her experience has led her to believe that personal power can come through healing our own wounds, accepting life's lessons, developing an intimate relationship with nature, and initiating actions which grow out of love for ourselves, other people, and our world.

Elizabeth A. Smith is recently divorced after a fifteen year marriage. She has two children and works as a registered nurse. She recently received her B.A. in English, and would like to go on to graduate school. Ever since she was a little girl she has written poems. She strongly believes that women who have been abused, whether physically, or psychologically as she was, need to tell their stories, "to educate our daughters so that these abuses are not continued through another generation."

John Sokol is an artist and writer who currently lives in Pittsburgh. His art has appeared on, or within the covers of, *Anteaus, Berkeley Poetry Review, The Faulkner Journal*, the *Georgia Review*, and on the covers of books by the University presses of Oxford, Princeton, Wisconsin, and Tennessee. His short stories and poetry have been published in various journals and reviews around the country.

Jane Steckbeck is a dedicated athlete who spends her spare time cycling, running, lifting weights and swimming. She also regularly plays co-ed soft ball and volleyball, and recently completed her first one-hundred mile bike ride. After practicing law for five years, Jane left the legal profession to join the faculty at the University of Oregon law school where she works as a career counselor. Jane lives with her husband, Ed, and three cats, Turtle, Sunspot and Licorice. She believes that every woman should regularly take self-defense training.

Jennifer Stone's selected essays on literature and politics, *Stone's Throw* (Berkeley: North American Books) won the 1989 Before Columbus American Book Award. Her essays on film and television were published in *Mind Over Media* (Berkeley: Cayuse Press, 1988). Her most recent novel, *Telegraph Avenue Then: Loose Leaves from a Little Black Book 1966-'77* was published by Regent Press in 1992. Currently, she hosts a weekly Pacifica radio program on literature, broadcast every Thursday morning at 8:10 AM on KPFA-FM 94.1 in Berkeley, California.

Kent Taylor got his start in the Cleveland, Ohio poetry scene of the 1960s where his first book was published by d. a. levy's renegade press in 1963. These days he lives in San Francisco where he continues to write. His most recent book is *Rabbits Have Fled* (Black Rabbit Press, Cleveland, 1991), and his poems have also appeared in many literary reviews, such as *Rain City Review, On the Bus, Abraxas,* and *Wormwood Review.*

Paul Truttman was born in Sacramento, California in 1947, and was raised in Bognor Regis, England and in Auckland, New Zealand. He served twenty-one years in the United States Navy, and was deployed along the coasts of Vietnam and Lebanon. Although he is currently incarcerated in San Quentin, it is his goal to take his negative experience and produce long-lasting and productive results. He wants to make very clear that his writing is not intended to glorify his actions or his wife's death, but to make peace.

Sheila S. Velazquez is currently working on a collection of short fiction. She lives in Nashville, Tennessee.

Yvonne Vowels recently completed a Ph.D. in Comparative Religion and Women's Studies from the Graduate Theological Union in Berkeley, California, and is currently a self-employed writer/educator/editor/counselor in Eugene, Oregon, with one foot in the academic world and the other in the alternative healing community. In her ongoing quest for psychological healing and spiritual liberation, she has frequently employed the geographic cure, moving forty-two times in her forty-two years on the planet: from Lansing, Michigan, to Los Angeles, Red Bluff, and Berkeley, California, to Tokyo, Japan, to Eugene, etc. A practicing Vajrayana Buddhist of Irish/American ancestry, Yvonne dreams of one day visiting Ireland with her mother in order to explore her pagan roots.

D. M. Wallace began writing poetry as a teenager and has been blessed with many insightful teachers and poet-mentors along the way. In 1982, Silverfish Review Press published her chapbook, *White Hannah.* As well, her poems have appeared in many literary magazines and anthologies. In addition to poetry, Wallace also writes film reviews and criticism, having earned her B. A. in Telecommunications and Film from the University of Oregon in 1989. Currently, she lives in Eugene, Oregon, where she is raising her sons, working at a winery, and occasionally teaching poetry classes to children and adults.

Jeff Walt earned his M. F. A. at Goddard College in Vermont. His poems have appeared in several magazines and in the anthologies, *Gents, Bad Boys and Barbarians* (Alyson Publications, 1995) and *Writing Our Way Out of the Dark: An Anthology by Child Abuse Survivors* (Queen of Swords Press, 1995). He was also recently awarded a fellowship at the MacDowell Colony in Peterborough, New Hampshire.

Lenore Baeli Wang is currently running a poetry workshop at Agapé House, a homeless shelter in Somerville, New Jersey. Her writing has received considerable notice with publications ranging from *Calyx, the Kelsey review, Sinister Wisdom,* and *Without Halos* to *Mr. Cogito* and *Kalliope.* In 1992, she was awarded a Ucross residency. Her chapbook, *Born in the Year of the Pink Sink* is recently out from Malafemmina Press. She teaches at Rider College in Lawrenceville, New Jersey, and is currently at work on a poetry manuscript entitled *Conversations with Emily (Dickinson).*

A native Oregonian, **Rebecca Whetstine** has recently returned home after sixteen years away. She has survived the usual complement of life's vicissitudes (rapes, battering, "inappropriate touching") and had more than her share of pleasures as she made the circuit from San Francisco to Los Angeles to Nevada to Oklahoma to New York City to various points in Europe. She currently works as an AIDS researcher, and makes her home in Portland, Oregon, where she lives with her Cherokee son and a garden that is out of control.

Kennette Harrison Wilkes writes, "The mother who battered and abused me when she was her 'other self,' is the same mother who jumped up in the sedate audience and shouted like a cheer leader when I got my M.A. in Creative Writing after having attended classes in a reclining lawn chair at middle age while suffering from a debilitating illness. Writing has been my best medicine."

Kimmika L. H. Williams is a poet, playwright, and performance artist, currently living in Darby, Pennsylvania. Wife, mother, teacher, actress, director, she is the Faculty Fellow in Playwriting at Temple University's graduate theater Department. With over eleven professional stage productions to her credit, she is also the author of *Negro Kinship to the Park, Halley's Comet, It Ain't Easy to be Different, God Made Men Brown* and *Epic Memory.* In addition, she has been widely published in a variety of venues, including *Poets and Writers, Black America,* and *The Philadelphia Daily News.* Her adventures as a recording artist include a 45-minute cassette, *Don't Call Me Bitch*(1985) on the Mark Hyman Associates label.

Dawn Diez Willis has been published in a variety of national journals, including *Zyzzyva, Southern Poetry Review* and *Visions-International.* She has received the Jessamyn West Award for Poetry and an Oregon Literary Arts fellowship for her first novel-in-progress, *Love Sick.* "The Arc of Wings" is from her unpublished manuscript, *The Brilliance of Flesh.*

Emboldened by a grant from Oregon Literary Arts, as well as by residences at Hedgebrook Cottages for Women Writers and the Ragdale Foundation, **Hannah Wilson** is completing *Cables*, a novel told in prose and poetry about two women who learned how to darn their world: the Homeric Penelope and her contemporary counterpart, Nola, wife of a soldier missing in Vietnam. Hannah lives with her husband (and dogs) in Eugene, where for three years she served as the Fiction Editor of *Northwest Review.*

M. Tarn Wilson lives in Saratoga, California, and works as a high school English teacher in alternative education. She earned a B. A. in English from Principia College and an M. A. in education from Stanford University. Her work has been published on the Home Forum Page of the *Christian Science Monitor.*

Leilani Wright's work has appeared in *Hayden's Ferry Review, Christian Science Monitor, Exquisite Corpse* and *Hawai'i Review*, among other publications. A chapbook, *Natural Good Shot* was published by Coffee Store Press in 1994. Winner of the 1996 Tucson Poetry Festival Award, she is also co-editor with James Cervantes of *Fever Dreams*, an anthology of contemporary Arizona poetry, due out in 1997 from the University of Arizona Press.

Androna Zawinski's book, *Traveling in Reflected Light*, was recently released from Pig Iron Press as the Kenneth Patchen Competition winner. Her poetry has appeared in *Callaloo, Poets On, Painted Bride* and elsewhere with work forthcoming in *Sistersong: Women Across Cultures,* and others. She is currently finalizing a new manuscript, *The Same Sky Everywhere.*

PUBLICATION ACKNOWLEDGMENTS

Queen of Swords Press gratefully acknowledges the editors of the publications listed below in which some of the works included in this anthology first appeared. All writings are reprinted in *Hard Love* with the permission of their author.

Kim Addonizio's story, "Inside Out" previously appeared *Five Fingers Review* #7(1989) in a slightly different form; her poems, "Cranes in August" and "The Taste of Apples," were included in her collection, *The Philosophers' Club* (BOA Editions, 1994). Thomas Avena's poem, "Land's End," was published in *Northwest Review* (1992). Ellyn Bache's story, "The Value of Kindness," appeared previously in her collection of the same title, published by Helicon Nine Editions, 1993. Jane Relaford Brown's poem "War Zone" was first published in 1993 in the anthology,*The Flight of the Eagle: Poetry on the U.S.-Mexico Border/ El Vuelo del Aguila: Poesia en al Frontera Mexico-Estados Unidos* (Binational Press). Renny Christopher's poem, "There Is No Bootcamp for Viet Nam Vets' Wives," was included in her collection, *Viet Nam and California* (Viet Nam Generation/ Burning Cities Press). Elizabeth Claman's poems were previously included in the following publications: "Kenel, South Dakota" in *Fireweed* (Fall 1991), "At the Movies" in *Hubbub* (winter 1990-91), and "Snow" in *Silverfish Review* (winter 1992). Barbara Crooker's "For a Friend Who Thinks About Going Back . . ." appeared in *Athena* (1989), and "Why You Don't Have to Be Afraid . . ." in *Thirteen* (1991). Martha Clark Cummings' story, "The Dutchess," was part of her fiction collection, *Mono Lake* (Rowbarge Press, 1995). Philip Dacey's "Why He Beat Her" appeared in *Hurakan: A Journal of Contemporary Literature* (1995). Sue Doro's poem, "Ruthie," appears in a slightly different version in her book, *Heart, Home and Hard Hats* (Midwest Villages and Voices, 1986). Sharon Doubiago's poem, "Outlaw," was previously part of her collection, *Psyche Drives the Coast* (Empty Bowl Press, 1990). Molly Fisk's poem, "Walking Down Franklin Street" appeared in Poetry East (summer 1994). Amy Klauke-Minato's poem, "The Wider Lens," was included in *Desert Ramblings* (1996). Claudia E. Lapp's poem, "Darning the World," appeared in *Mothering* magazine (Fall 1991), and in *Véhicule Days*, (Montreal: Nu Age Editions, 1993). Dorianne Laux's three poems, "Afterwards," "Enough Music," and "Kissing" were all previously published in her collection,*What We Carry* (BOA Editions, 1994). "A Falling Woman" by Rachel Loden appeared in *Cumberland Poetry Review*. Katharyn Howd Machan's poem, "Battered," was first published in *Rag Times: A Feminist Monthly* (1983). Chris Mandell's "Thoughts After a Rape" was included in *What's a Nice Girl Like You Doing in a Relationship Like This*. Judith Neva's poem "Helping My Daughter Pack" appeared previously in *Swamp Root* #5 (1990). Linda Peavy's story, "The Kill Floor," was first published in *Athena* (1989) and later included in the anthology,*Word of Mouth: Short Fiction by Women* (1990). "The Beater's Wife" by Amudha Rajendran first appeared in *Feed*. Willa Schneberg's poem, "Bedding Down" was first published in *Women's Review of Books* (1985) and in a slightly different form, "The Bells of St. Bavo Sing Scat" appeared in *Jacaranda* (1996). Brenda Shaw's poem, "Lucky," appeared in her chapbook *Too Cold to Snow* (Infinity Press, 1993). John Sokol's poem, "Sestina for Parting Jagged," appeared in *The Pittsburgh Quarterly* (1992). Jennifer Stone's piece is excerpted from her autobiographical novel, *Telegraph Avenue Then* (Regent Press, 1992). D. M. Wallace's poem, "Eros," was published in 1991 in *Calypso Journal of Narrative Poetry and Poetic Fiction.* Jeff Walt's poem, "The Smell of Sex," appeared in 1995 in *Christopher Street;* "Where We Lived" was previously published in *New York Native* (1996). Lenore Baeli Wang's poem, "Battered Woman's Alphabet" first came out in *Downtown Magazine* (1993). Kimmika L. H. Williams' poem, "Nine Years Down the Drain," appeared in her collection, *Envisioning a Sea of Dry Bones.* Dawn Diez Willis' poem, "The Arc of Wings," first appeared in *The Willamette Journal of the Liberal Arts.* Hannah Wilson's "Certain Slants of Light" appeared in *Calapooya Collage* (1992). Leilani Wright's "Blood Words" was previously published in *Psychopoetica* (vol. 30).